SCARE POLLUTION

ALSO BY STEVE MILLOY

Science-Based Risk Assessment:
A Piece of the Superfund Puzzle
(1995)

~

Science Without Sense:
The Risky Business of Public Health Research
(1995)

~

Silencing Science
(1999)

~

Junk Science Judo:
Self Defense Against Health Scares and Scams
(2001)

~

Green Hell:
How Environmentalist Plan to Control Your Life and What You Can Do to Stop Them
(2009)

STEVE MILLOY

Scare Pollution

Why and How to Fix the EPA

First edition published 2016 by Bench Press
First eBook edition published 2016 by Bench Press

ISBN 978-0-9982597-1-0

Interior layout by MrLasers.com

PRINTED IN THE UNITED STATES OF AMERICA

Contents

Preface

Few Americans would imagine that the intersection of such seemingly staid endeavors as scientific research, environmental regulation, federal bureaucracy, public health and the law known as The Freedom of Information Act could yield an alarming narrative of concocted dangers and contorted science designed to expand the reach of an already-too-powerful federal agency. Yet, as you shall see, this book details how the U.S. Environmental Protection Agency (EPA) has over the course of the last 20 years marshaled its vast and virtually unchallenged power into an echo chamber of deceptive science, runaway regulations and fatally-flawed research derived from un-ethical human experiments. The EPA's conduct runs the gamut from subtle statistical shenanigans to withholding key scientific data, from seeking to rubberstamp baseless research data to illegally spraying diesel exhaust up the noses of unsuspecting children and other vulnerable populations.

There are significant obstacles one faces when presenting a shocking story of the brazen politicization—the ideological hijacking, if you will—of a vast federal entity and the perversion of its mission. Chief among these obstacles is disbelief. In an effort to dispel the reader's understandable disbelief, every effort has been made to present this narrative in a thoroughly documented fashion: The necessary and myriad facts are presented in the sequence in which they occurred or were uncovered. Exact quotes from agency sources and relevant outside contacts are used and footnoted extensively throughout, allowing the EPA and their many allies to hoist themselves upon their own petards. Wherever possible, every effort has been made to simplify complex scientific or statistical concepts and language for the layperson. And finally, after the reader has been walked through this twisted tale of regulatory abuse, suggestions for curtailing the EPA's out-of-control authority are offered.

We all want a clean and safe environment. But contrary to what we typically hear from the media, environmental activists, the federal government—not to mention what generations of alarmed schoolchildren have been taught—our environment has always been remarkably *safe* despite more than 150 years of industrial development. This message has been so suppressed by the media, environmental activists and the EPA itself that, for the vast majority of people, it is downright shocking to hear. Nevertheless, it is reality.

Although the public has almost always been safe, our environment has not always been so clean. This is most recently and vividly evidenced by the urban smog and river fires of the early- to mid-20th century. So beginning with the Clean Air Act of 1963, which was followed by major amendments to the law in 1970 and 1977, America embarked on an aggressive campaign to clean its environment.

In a December 1970 Executive Order—done largely as a cynical sop to anti-Vietnam War activists—President Richard Nixon consolidated virtually all federal agency environmental activities into a new organization called the U.S. Environmental Protection Agency. Although never officially organized by Congress as a Presidential cabinet-level department, subsequent laws were nevertheless written and passed to be implemented by Nixon's new bureaucratic invention. The EPA's odd status as an incredibly powerful federal agency without cabinet-level status continues to this day.

Through a combination of factors—including new laws, public pressure, industrial innovation and technology, national wealth, the beginning of globalization and a decline in domestic heavy industry—our environment had in fact by 1990 become remarkably cleaner. Though the government and environmental activists like to take exclusive credit for the improvement in our environment, it was primarily brought about by a society with far greater awareness and concern for its environment and with the necessary wealth to achieve its desired ends.

At that time, the environmental debate in the U.S. should have turned to consider at what point was an even cleaner environment simply not worth the cost. Instead, the debate was hijacked by a confluence of historical events and the "industrialization" of the environmental movement.

The precipitous end of the Cold War resulted in the disbanding of the peace movement. Left-wing political activists suddenly became rebels without a cause. As documented by former left-wing radicals like Greenpeace-co-founder Patrick Moore and New Left activist-journalist David Horowitz, many flocked from the peace movement to the environmental movement.

Activist groups that started out as rag-tag bands or niche groups soon became financial powerhouses. Greenpeace, for example, had revenues of $100 million annually by 1986. So environmental protection became a politicized ideology powered by a highly profitable business model.

The EPA was transformed in a similar way. From its $1 billion annual budget and 4,000 employees in 1970, the EPA expanded into a $6 billion annual budget with 16,000 employees by 1991. President Ronald Reagan's first EPA Administrator, Anne Gorsuch tried to rein in the EPA's already evident excesses. But a Democrat-controlled Congress armed with Gorsuch's own petty transgressions hounded her from office.

President Reagan replaced Gorsuch with William Ruckelshaus, who had been the EPA's first administrator under President Nixon. But unknown to President Reagan, Ruckelshaus was also a fundraising member of the radical activist group, the Environmental Defense Fund and was not about to restrain the EPA's activities. It would be more than a decade before anyone seriously discussed reining in the EPA again.

I first started working on issues involving the EPA in 1990. As a young lawyer-statistician working for a regulatory agency lobbying firm, I immediately began work on a number of EPA issues. Each time I dove into their various scientific and economic details, I entered a weird and wacky world of overregulation.

Take, for example, the valuable and widely used pesticide called Aldicarb, which had been used safely for years by farmers to increase yields of potatoes and citrus fruits. The EPA wanted to ban it because laboratory experiment results showed that, if you essentially poisoned dogs with the pesticide, the dogs might temporarily have soft stool. Aside from the fact that dogs would never be exposed to Aldicarb in the first place, the regulatory debate boiled down to what sort of dog stool is too soft and is that an adverse health effect for purposes of regulation?

Another odd regulatory fight was over phosphoric acid, which is used by food and beverage manufacturers, for example, to give soft drinks a tangy taste. Although the Food and Drug Administration had classified phosphoric acid for decades as "generally recognized as safe," the chemical had been inadvertently been listed as a toxic substance by Congress when it enacted the Emergency Planning and Community Right-to-Know Act in the wake of the 1984 Bhopal gas plant disaster. Though phosphoric acid was in no way related to what happened in Bhopal, because of the EPA listing, the FDA was considering removing its "generally recognized as safe status (GRAS)."

Then there was the question of the economic value of blue sky and whether it could be ascertained by surveying people about how much they would personally pay to have blue sky. The people surveyed would never actually have to pay anything. But whatever they said they would pay was then going to be used in determining how much businesses should actually pay in the event they decreased the blueness of the sky.

Amid the EPA-induced 1980s hysteria about naturally-occurring radioactive radon gas being emitted from basement foundations and supposedly increasing the risk of lung cancer, the agency wanted to evacuate residents and demolish homes in the town of Pocatello, Idaho. The EPA claimed that when it flew an airplane over the community, it had measured elevated levels of radon gas being emitted by the homes' foundations, which had been made of concrete composed of local mining waste. Despite the lack of any credible science showing that the low-levels of radon being emitted were dangerous or showing any increased incidence of lung cancer among residents who had lived in the homes for decades, the EPA was on the warpath scaring residents and depressing property values.

The last example is one that still resonates today amid the current alarm over global warming. Though Congress had instructed the Department of Energy to prepare a long-term storage facility for spent radioactive fuel from nuclear power plants, the anti-nuclear power EPA was doing its best to gum up the works. Although the facility to be constructed at Yucca Mountain, Nevada was in the desert, a hundred miles from anywhere and a mile underground, the EPA was trying to decide whether the Yucca Mountain storage site should be made safe from intruders and leakage for one million years or only 10,000 years. Never mind that all of recorded history is only about 5,000 years old.

But the EPA won anyway. It dragged out the process so long it became possible for President Obama, as one of his first official acts, to kill the Yucca Mountain project. Although the EPA believes that carbon dioxide emissions from power plants need to be reduced, nuclear power is one way to do so and existing nuclear power plants are running out of space for storing spent nuclear fuel, the Yucca Mountain project is no longer on the drawing board.

The only thing more absurd than these baseless controversies— each of which was causing or could cause genuine but unjustified economic harm to businesses, manufacturers and our economy—was the agency behind them.

In the more than 25 years since, things have not only failed to improve; they've become more bizarre. Every EPA issue I've ever worked—whether air pollution, water pollution, toxic waste sites, pesticides, chemical safety, hazardous waste, non-hazardous waste and radiation—has been an exercise akin to arguing over how many angels can dance on the head of a pin. And although the EPA's science is often unsubstantiated, it has real world costs. Those costs include lost jobs, squandered taxpayer money, misplaced government priorities, high business costs, lost business opportunities, lost income, lost personal freedom, more inconvenience and a lower standard of living to name a few.

One could go on about the burdensome nature of overregulation. Volumes have already been written about the abuses and harms caused by the EPA.

But one EPA malfeasance stands out more than others. That issue is a type of air pollution that the EPA calls "fine particulate matter" or PM2.5 (pronounced P-M-2-point-5). PM2.5 is very small dust or soot in the air, some of which is released by natural sources like volcanoes and forest fires and some of which is manmade. The EPA's view of PM2.5 essentially is that it is the most toxic substance known to man. There is no safe exposure to PM2.5 and any exposure can kill you within hours—according to the EPA, that is.

Fittingly, PM2.5 has been central to the EPA's regulatory agenda for the past 20 years. The EPA's most prominent, burdensome and expensive regulations all are based on it. PM2.5 is an issue that the EPA has exploited to exercise complete control over the energy, transportation and industrial sectors—in short, a large and vital part of the U.S. economy.

Most dramatically, the EPA has been able to destroy about 90 percent of the market value of the U.S. coal industry through PM2.5 regulation. Even President Obama's controversial global warming rules known as the "Clean Power Plan" were actually more based on controlling PM2.5 emissions than carbon dioxide emissions from coal-fired power plants. As a result, the largest publicly owned coal companies have all filed for bankruptcy. Thousands of well-paying and wealth-creating coal industry jobs have been lost. Tens of thousands of more jobs have been lost in supporting industries. Unemployment and loss of tax revenues has ravaged coal mining communities—areas in which most of the best paying jobs were in the coal industry.

The EPA and its supporters have attempted to minimize the impact on the coal industry of President Obama's so-called "war on coal" by pointing to the phenomenon of low-cost natural gas brought on by the concurrent development of hydrofracturing ("fracking") technology. Their claim is that natural gas is a less expensive fuel for electric utilities to burn and, so, utilities have logically switched to it. But this assertion is disingenuous.

At most, natural gas is now only cost-competitive with coal, not less expensive. As President Obama's war on coal has produced new rules and tremendous political pressure on utilities to cut emissions of everything from PM2.5 to carbon dioxide, utilities are opting wherever they can to switch from coal to natural gas. The latter is not less expensive; it's just relatively more politically correct. And the claimed lethality of PM2.5 has been a key component in the Obama administration's demonization of coal.

But the EPA's PM2.5 regulatory weapon is not just aimed at coal. Keeping in mind that PM2.5 is fine soot and dust, the EPA and its regulatory allies in states—especially California—have used PM2.5 rules to target the oil and gas, manufacturing, forest and paper and trucking industries, to name just a few. The EPA was even considering regulating PM2.5 from farms and agricultural facilities, but was forced to publicly disavow the idea ahead of the 2012 elections.

Even EPA regulations that are ostensibly not about PM2.5 rely on the agency's claims about PM2.5. In addition to the previously mentioned global warming rules, the EPA's rules for ground-level ozone or smog—alleged by industry to be the most expensive EPA regulations ever—were actually 90 percent justified on the basis that they would also reduce PM2.5 emissions. The EPA's PM2.5 rules are so strict that states choose to forgo economic development rather than risk running afoul of the EPA's rules.

So the public is being frightened, jobs are being lost and industries and communities are being ruined. Wealth-creating and poverty-ending economic activity is being restrained and destroyed. Government employees and contractors at universities appear to be rubberstamping EPA's distorted claims. The EPA is using dishonest means to expand its regulatory power. This is all happening because of and through the EPA's patently and demonstrably false claim that PM2.5 kills people.

Despite the best efforts of the EPA and its allies to prevent discovery of the scientific misinformation behind PM2.5, this book presents, uncovers and debunks in one unified narrative this miscarriage of science against our society. But this David vs. Goliath story goes beyond just the EPA.

The EPA's allies in this affront have included other federal and state regulatory agencies, universities and their researchers, federal courts, state medical boards, scientific journals, environmental activist groups, bioethicists, Congress and even the directly-harmed victims of the EPA's regulations—industries themselves.

If you respect science, you will read about how the EPA has abused and dishonored it. If you value government integrity, you will read about how the EPA has mocked it. If you prize a clean environment, you will read how the EPA wastes significant societal resources accomplishing nothing. Indeed, if you respect human life itself, you will be appalled at what the EPA has tried to do to unsuspecting people in the name of regulation.

If you were in the coal industry and you wonder where your job went, you're going to find out how the EPA killed it. If you're a trucker and wonder why the government is forcing you to spend tens of thousands of dollars to pointlessly upgrade your already low-emission truck engine, well, this book will just make you shake your head in disgust. If you're a consumer, particularly one on a fixed income, the EPA's war on PM2.5 is raising the cost of electricity, gasoline, cars, home and garden equipment and much more—all without any benefit to you, society or the environment. The EPA has spent hundreds of millions of taxpayer dollars perpetrating the myths about PM2.5 described here. While this book will discuss all the relevant historical, scientific and statistical evidence that debunk the EPA's claims, in the end any layman could do the same armed with data on cigarettes or marijuana joints or hookah pipes—as this book will explain. It's so frightfully simple to prove them wrong, you will wonder how the EPA gets away with it.

This story may also serve as a roadmap for those wishing to challenge seemingly impregnable government scientific authority. Throughout, every imaginable way to tackle the EPA is attempted. These efforts range from using the Freedom of Information Act, to uncovering embarrassing revelations, to agitating for legislation, to suing the EPA and even conducting and publishing original scientific research. No stone has been left unturned. No avenue untried.

And yet, the EPA is still acting badly. But no one who has followed this story as it has unfolded on my web site JunkScience.com—and that includes many members of Congress—will ever look at the EPA the same. More importantly, this struggle against the EPA continues.

Over the years as this story has unfolded, I have enjoyed a great deal of moral and intellectual support from a number of special people. The ones that stand out the most include my wife Julia, Francis Collins, Dr. John Dale Dunn, Dr. S. Stanley Young, Vera Sharav, Lee Brown, Dr. James Enstrom and Dr. David Schnare. This story would not have been possible without them. While I am eternally grateful for their help and proud of my work, I wish that this effort had not been necessary. It is appalling that our government operates this way—and calls it "science."

Introduction

I was doing my usual daily round of research for my website JunkScience.com on September 15, 2011, when this new study with its mouthful of a title popped up:

Case Report: Supraventricular Arrhythmia Following Exposure to Concentrated Ambient Air Pollution Particles

Translation: Someone's heart started fluttering after they had inhaled a jacked-up level of outdoor air pollution.

Reading that scientists from the U.S. Environmental Protection Agency (EPA) were involved, my own heart began to race a little. Would this report make me retract a very public attack on the EPA—a July 11, 2011 op-ed for the Washington Times that was brazenly titled, "Show us the bodies, EPA."

The op-ed was occasioned by an EPA proposal to saddle Midwest coal-fired power plants with yet more expensive smokestack emissions requirements. The Republican-controlled Congress was trying to stop the rule by cutting the agency's budget. Environmental activists came to the EPA's aid by running ads claiming that the EPA's opponents were pushing a "dirty air" bill that would kill 17,000 people per year. The claim was based on a 1996 determination of the EPA's that outdoor air killed people—even though the Clean Air Act had been enacted more than 30 years earlier.

Long a doubter of the EPA's claim that typical outdoor air pollution killed tens of thousands of people every year, I had challenged the agency in "Show Us the Bodies, EPA," as follows:

> *The EPA says air pollution kills tens of thousands of people annually. This is on a par with traffic accident fatalities. While we can identify traffic accident victims, air pollution victims are unknown, unidentified and as far as anyone can tell, figments of the EPA's statistical imagination.*
>
> *It ought not to be too much to ask the EPA to produce some tangible evidence that air pollution is causing actual harm to real people. The EPA should have to demonstrate that its ever-tightening air quality and emissions standards are producing actual benefits.*
>
> *Consider that the EPA and its enviro-buddies are essentially accusing coal-fired utilities of killing and injuring hundreds of thousands of people annually. Have you ever wondered why there are no class-action lawsuits against utilities for billions of dollars in damages?*

Now while the case report's headline didn't involve any deaths per se, it did involve a heart abnormality that could lead to death. But after scanning a few pages of the report, any anxiety I had vanished.

The person who experienced the heartbeat irregularity turned out to be a 58-year- old woman who not only was obese and suffering from hypertension and other maladies, she had a family history of heart disease—her father had died from heart disease when he was 57 years old. So there was no way that whatever happened to her could be conclusively blamed on air pollution, concentrated or not. Plain and simple, this woman was an ambulance trip waiting to happen.

So "Show me the bodies, EPA" remained as sound a challenge as ever. The question then became, how did this poor, sick woman come to be exposed to "concentrated ambient air particles" in the first place? Where and how did that happen?

Reading further, it turned out that EPA scientists had intentionally made this woman inhale the concentrated air particles. They induced her to inhale air containing three times the maximum level of particles that the EPA allows in outdoor air. Though she was supposed to inhale this air for two hours, after about 20 minutes, her heart began to beat erratically. At this point the EPA researchers stopped the experiment and called an ambulance to take her to the hospital. Though her heart beat quickly returned to normal, she remained in the hospital overnight.

Needless to say, this was all quite astounding. To explain just how astounding it was, let's fast-forward the story one week to September 22, 2011 when EPA Administrator, Lisa Jackson, testified before a subcommittee of the House Energy and Commerce Committee. During her testimony, Administrator Jackson stated:

> *Particulate matter causes premature death. It doesn't make you sick. It's directly causal to dying sooner than you should.*

The "particulate matter" she referred to was the same sort of air particles to which the 58-year-old woman had been exposed—except, of course, that the particles the woman inhaled were "concentrated" and so, one would reasonably suppose, even more dangerous than those in typical outdoor air.

So EPA scientists had made a sick woman inhale something that the EPA Administrator had described to Congress as something that would kill you. Go straight to Death. Do not pass Sick. That was the EPA's story.

CHAPTER 1

The EPA's Secondhand Smoke-and-Mirrors

"Show us the bodies." Where did *that* come from, other than a very funny Cuba Gooding, Jr.-Tom Cruise scene in *Jerry Maguire*? The story goes back to the early 1990s when I worked as a consultant at Multinational Business Services for a colorful guy named Jim Tozzi.

A career bureaucrat until he had to pay for his kids' college, Tozzi rose to power as a key government overseer of the budgets and rulemaking efforts of regulatory agencies like the EPA. He was the driving force behind a major Reagan administration policy requiring the benefits of regulations to exceed their costs. And he enforced that principle like no one has since.

I was hired by Tozzi because I was both a lawyer and had a background in science and statistics, the perfect combination for Tozzi's plan to expand his lobbying practice to include environment and health risk assessment issues. One of the first issues I worked on was the EPA's risk assessment of secondhand smoke. As a nonsmoker, I wasn't especially thrilled about working on a tobacco issue. But the EPA soon fixed that.

The EPA in 1990 had issued a draft risk assessment document in which the agency presented its evidence for concluding that secondhand smoke caused lung cancer in humans and that secondhand smoke caused 3,000 deaths from lung cancer every year. These claims were largely based on approximately 30 studies of lung cancer in various human populations exposed to secondhand smoke. Such studies of disease in human populations are called "epidemiology."

Epidemiologic studies can be very useful in the practice of public health. The classic example is food poisoning where epidemiologic evidence can be used to trace the origin of the outbreak. Epidemiology has also been used to link heavy smoking with lung cancer and aspirin with Reyes syndrome in children, to provide a just a couple notable and creditable examples. But the epidemiologic method can be abused and the EPA was working on perfecting just how to do that with secondhand smoke.

The key to the value of epidemiology as an investigative tool is that a researcher must be looking for a relatively high rate of a relatively rare event in a human population. The reason for this is that epidemiology is just statistics applied to the incidence of disease in human population. Epidemiologic results are essentially correlations and, as we all learn in Statistics 101, correlations do not equate to causation.

A quick example of the correlation-is-not-causation principle is the very high correlation between per capita margarine consumption in the U.S. and divorce rate in Maine. As the consumption of margarine declined during the 2000s, it did so in nearly the same rate—a 99 percent match—as the divorce rate in Maine.[1] So although the changes in margarine consumption and the divorce rate in Maine correlate very highly (that is at a 99 percent level), there is no causal connection between the two phenomena. That is, Americans eating less margarine does not cause Mainers to divorce less or vice versa.

But if a researcher can find a high rate of a rare disease in a population with a specific exposure of interest, she may very well be on the way to drawing a connection between the exposure and disease. The high rate and rare disease combination is a good reason to investigate the potential relationship to see if it is causal. In contrast, trying to use epidemiology to connect a low rate of a common disease with a specific exposure is typically not very persuasive—that is, until the EPA turned the epidemiology world upside down with its secondhand smoke risk assessment.

Of the 30 or so epidemiologic studies cited in the EPA's risk assessment, the results for about 80 percent of the studies either failed to show a correlation between exposure to secondhand smoke and lung cancer incidence, or the reported correlation was not statistically significant—meaning that the results were too likely to have been caused by chance to be used as evidence that secondhand smoke was causally related to lung cancer. This was a problem for the EPA, which had decided before it had even started its risk assessment what the outcome would be.

Further, the other 20 percent of the studies all reported very low or weak correlations between exposure to secondhand smoke and lung cancer. As such they ran afoul of the cardinal rule against relying on studies reporting low rates of disease. But the EPA had a plan—or rather a recipe—for cooking its secondhand smoke risk assessment.

To eliminate the problem posed by the 80 percent of the studies that couldn't correlate secondhand smoke with lung cancer, the EPA took the results of all 30 studies and combined them into one big study with a statistical technique called "meta-analysis."

The purpose of the meta-analysis technique is to convert a bunch of statistically small and meaningless studies into a single larger more statistically meaningful study. While meta-analysis is a perfectly reasonable way to combine smaller and similarly conducted studies, it is entirely inappropriate when the studies being combined have all been conducted in significantly different ways, as is typical with epidemiology. Mixing apples and oranges is a good metaphor for combining epidemiologic studies through meta-analysis.

Undaunted by the impropriety of conducting a meta-analysis of the secondhand smoke epidemiologic studies, the EPA proceeded to produced a single, unified positive correlation between secondhand smoke and lung cancer. But the EPA still had a problem. Its concocted correlation was not statistically significant—meaning that the result could be due to chance. And under the EPA's own risk assessment guidelines, epidemiologic results had to be statistically significant to be considered reliable. But the ever-resourceful EPA had yet another card up its sleeve.

When epidemiologists (and most other scientists) test their results for statistical significance, they are looking for significance at a 95 percent level. That is, they want to have 95 percent confidence that their results did not occur by chance. Much to the EPA's dismay, its results were not statistically significant at the 95 percent level.

But EPA discovered that when the confidence level for its meta-analysis was reduced from 95 percent to 90 percent, the meta-analysis result magically, but barely, attained something EPA felt it could call a "statistically significant" result. Now here's the evil genius of it: EPA's risk assessment guidelines only indicated that epidemiologic results needed to be statistically significant—they did not indicate what that level of statistical significance had to be. So for EPA, it was bye-bye 95 percent, hello 90 percent.

What's the big deal? 95 percent confidence versus 90 percent confidence? Aren't they pretty much the same? For one thing, by switching from the conventional 95 percent confidence level to the more convenient 90 percent confidence level, the size of the margin of error was doubled. Moreover, that bit of statistical flimflammery showed just how determinedly desperate EPA was to link secondhand smoke with lung cancer. It wasn't conventional or really even honest statistics.

But even accepting this statistical trick, the EPA's claims still ran afoul of the cardinal rule against relying on weak statistical correlations.

Consider that in a food poisoning epidemiology study, you may see 30 times more food poisoning among people who ate the food in question versus those who did not. With smoking and lung cancer, you'll see anywhere from 10 to 20 times more lung cancer in populations of heavy smokers as compared to nonsmokers. Populations of children given aspirin have 5 to 6 times more Reye's syndrome than those children who haven't taken aspirin. Those are all considered to be reliable epidemiologic results. Yet with secondhand smoke, the EPA was claiming statistical certainty with a mere 0.19 times more lung cancer among people exposed to secondhand smoke.

Discussions and meetings with EPA staff about the agency's statistical abuses made it clear the agency's story was that the epidemiology showed secondhand smoke caused 3,000 lung cancer deaths per year—and they were going to stick to it. The EPA staff was set on ignoring comments to the contrary as well as those of the independent science advisers. EPA Science Advisory Board member and New York University scientist Mort Lippman, for example, famously commented to EPA that the health risk from secondhand smoke was so small that it was "probably much less than you took to get [to the EPA building] through Washington traffic."

It was at this point that the EPA cured me of any qualms of working the secondhand smoke issue. Yes, secondhand smoke is unpleasant and annoying, but what the EPA was trying to do to science and public policy was worse. But not everyone was so concerned.

The EPA's use and abuse of the sort of weak correlation epidemiology was groundbreaking. In the late 1980s, EPA staff had tried to condemn diesel exhaust as a "known human" cancer causing substance using the same sort of epidemiology as for secondhand smoke, albeit without a meta-analysis. But the EPA's outside board of science advisors objected on the grounds that the correlations were weak and unconvincing and the diesel exhaust risk assessment document sank into oblivion.

I visited various trade associations in Washington, D.C. warning them of the terrible precedent the EPA was about to set through its secondhand smoke risk assessment. "Wait until the EPA applies this sort of statistical malpractice to you," they were warned. But they all knew better or thought they did. They knew that EPA could never—would never do that to them. They would never sink to the depths of political incorrectness occupied by the widely reviled tobacco industry. They would soon get quite a lesson from the agency.

Eventually a federal judge listening to the statistical atrocity committed by the EPA on secondhand smoke overturned the EPA's finding about lung cancer, finding in pertinent part that:

> *... In this case EPA publicly committed to a conclusion before research had begun . . . adjusted established procedure and scientific norms to validate the Agency's public conclusion . . . disregarded information and made findings on selective information; did not disseminate significant epidemiologic information; deviated from its Risk Assessment Guidelines; failed to disclose important findings and reasoning; and left significant questions without answers . . .*

And while this court decision was subsequently overturned on procedural grounds unrelated to the judge's review of the facts, it is clear that the only judge to ever become familiar with the EPA secondhand smoke risks assessment at a granular level was none too impressed with EPA's "science."

CHAPTER 2

Politics Over Science

I left the lobbying firm shortly after the EPA's risk assessment for secondhand smoke was finalized in December 1992 and I spent the next two years working with the U.S. Department of Energy to lead a study on the roles of science and politics in the setting of federal environmental policy.

At the time, the Energy Department was in the process of cleaning up the Cold War-era messes left by its nuclear weapons laboratories. It was concerned that the EPA would set impossible-to-meet cleanup standards. One of the Department's potential concerns was that EPA would force it to decontaminate its 1,360-square mile Nevada nuclear weapons testing site by vacuuming up the top inch of sand, decontaminating it and then re-spreading the decontaminated sand. The department was staring at hundreds of billions of dollars in cleanup costs.

So I put together a team and we spent a year interviewing hundreds of people from government, industry and environmental groups about the EPA risk assessment process. At the end, we produced a report called "Choices in Risk Assessment" that concluded that most environmental—that is, most EPA—policy was determined by politics rather than science. The report deconstructed in unprecedented detail the EPA-propagated myth that its decisions were driven by science.

The problem with the report was that, although it was the brain-child of the anti-EPA Energy Department of the Bush administration, it was completed under the Energy Department of the very pro-EPA Clinton administration. When the Office of the Secretary of Energy reviewed the report, I was called to the Secretary's office. Staff there told me in no uncertain terms that "Choices in Risk Assessment" did not come to the proper conclusions and so would not be published by the Department of Energy.

But I wasn't about to allow the hard work of my team to be deep-sixed by political correctness. So we published the report and distributed it on our own. "Choices in Risk Assessment" was important—and when the editorial page writers at the Wall Street Journal heard about the report, they thought so too.

When the Wall Street Journal spotlighted "Choices in Risk Assessment" in its lead editorial of December 6, 1994, requests for the report came in fast and furious.[2] By coincidence, the report had come on the heels of the Republican capture of Congress and was a perfect companion for Newt Gingrich's "Contract with America" platform that included a promise to reform the regulatory process. When the new Congress started in 1995, I was invited to testify by a Senate committee about the report.

In early 1995, Republicans had high hopes for reformulating how agencies like the EPA conducted risk assessments. They even expected such efforts to be bipartisan, as even the previous Democrat-controlled Congress had made noises about reforming how the EPA assessed risks to health and the environment. So legislation was drafted. Hearings were held. EPA reform looked possible. And then Carol Browner happened.

A former Al Gore staffer, Browner was appointed as EPA Administrator by President Bill Clinton. Faced with a hostile Congress looking to get a grip on the EPA's regulatory abuses, Browner went on the offensive. She accused Republicans of wanting to roll back environmental protection. "What this does is undermine every single environmental and public health standard in the country," Browner demagogued.[3]

While what she said was not remotely true, it served as a rallying point for EPA's political allies to come to the agency's aid. Between Republican political confusion, division and ineptitude on environment issues and Browner's demagoguery, regulatory reform of the EPA quietly faded away—at least as of the publication of this book.

The significance of Browner's triumph over the forces of regulatory reform was not so much that regulatory reform was stymied. But rather, it empowered and emboldened Browner to take EPA junk science to a new level—one that is the essence of this story.

CHAPTER 3

The EPA's Junk Science on Steroids

As stated previously, the Clean Air Act empowers the EPA to regulate outdoor air quality to a "safe" level. One of the substances in the air that EPA is required to regulate is so-called "particulate matter" or "PM."[4] PM can be natural (like dust, pollen, or soot from forest fires and volcanic eruptions) or it can be manmade (like soot from smokestacks, chimneys and tailpipes).

When EPA began regulating PM in 1971, it regulated relatively large pieces of dust and soot that were anywhere from 25 to 45 millionths of a meter (one to two thousandths of an inch) in diameter. In 1987, EPA revised its rules to focus on smaller bits of dust and soot that were 10 millionths of a meter in diameter (about half the width of a human hair)—so-called PM10 (pronounced P-M-ten). In November 1996 under Administrator Browner, EPA proposed to regulate even smaller bits of dust and soot, particles that were 2.5 millionths of a meter in width—so-called PM2.5 (pronounced P-M-two-point-five).[5]

The EPA's PM2.5 proposal wasn't particularly interesting except that the agency claimed its regulation of PM2.5 would save 20,000 lives per year, or in EPA parlance, prevent 20,000 premature deaths. Who knew that outdoor air in America was killing anyone, let alone due to something called PM2.5, which is both a naturally occurring and manmade substance? But maybe I was just ignorant, so I

15

investigated. Six weeks later, my findings on the EPA's "science" appeared on the pages of the Wall Street Journal.[6]

EPA had primarily based its 20,000-deaths claim on two epidemiologic studies, which we will refer to as the Harvard Six-City study[7] and the Pope study[8]. Both studies compared the death rates in cities with the highest level of PM2.5 with death rates in cities with the lowest level of PM2.5. The studies reported similar correlations between PM2.5 and death, 0.26 and 0.17 times more deaths in the "most polluted" versus the "least polluted" cities for the Harvard Six-City and the Pope studies, respectively.

That's right—zero-point-two-six and zero-point-one-seven, about the same size correlation as the EPA claimed for secondhand smoke that, as you will recall, was 0.19. The EPA's secondhand smoke railroad had come to outdoor air—but in even a worse way.

Recall that epidemiology is only useful for identifying strong correlations involving rare diseases or health events. While in the case of secondhand smoke, lung cancer was a suitably rare disease; the correlation (0.19 times more lung cancer among secondhand smokers versus non-secondhand smokers) was very weak, if not entirely contrived by EPA's statistical tricks.

With PM2.5 not only did EPA try to get by with weak correlations, but also a health endpoint that isn't particularly rare. Everyone, in fact, dies at some point. And fully one-half of the population dies before life expectancy. A weak correlation with a common health endpoint is not the hallmark of any health effect approaching meaningful epidemiology. A little more explanation about the Pope study will drive this point home.

The Pope study involved 295,223 adults who lived in 50 U.S. metropolitan areas. During the period of study, 1982-1989, 20,765 of these adults died. The Pope researchers computed that the death rate among people living in the "most polluted" metropolitan areas was 17 percent higher than among the people living in "least polluted" areas, after statistically adjusting for some other risk factors for death including age, sex, race, body-weight, whether they smoked, how much they drank, workplace risk factors and education.

While this may seem pretty straightforward, the proverbial devil is in the details that were overlooked or ignored by the EPA. First, the researchers had no idea how much PM2.5 any study subject inhaled during the period of study. Instead, the researchers simply assumed that study subjects inhaled whatever level of PM2.5 was computed from a formula—that is, the median PM2.5 level measured in the subject's metropolitan area by the EPA during the years 1979 through 1983. There was a lot wrong with this formula.

For many study subjects, this formula overestimated how much PM2.5 they inhaled because EPA air monitors tend to be placed near where the emissions happen, like major roads and industrial facilities, not where people actually inhale them, like inside their homes and workplaces. For other study subjects, this formula underestimated how much PM2.5 they inhaled because PM2.5 levels indoors, including in homes and workplaces, can be much higher than outside. Moreover, at the time the PM2.5 measurements used in the Pope study were taken, the federal watchdog U.S. General Accounting Office (GAO) had determined that EPA's air quality monitoring network was not reliable.[9]

And then there is the all-important phenomenon of smoking, which blows away outdoor air when it comes to inhaling particulate matter, including PM2.5. In 1980, about one-third of U.S. adults smoked.[10] In the Pope study population, 21.6 percent of the subjects actively smoked about one pack of cigarettes per day and another 29.4 percent of them formerly smoked one pack per day.

As C. Arden Pope himself admitted in 2009, a smoker will inhale on average about 12,000 millionths-of-a-gram of PM2.5 per cigarette.[11] That means a smoker smoking a pack of cigarettes per day will inhale, on average, 288,000 millionths-of-a-gram of PM2.5 per day. So how much PM2.5 was contained in the average outdoor air inhaled by the Pope study subjects? A mere 18 millionths-of-a-gram of PM2.5 per cubic meter of air. As an adult will typically breathe about a cubic meter of air per hour, an average day's worth of inhaled PM2.5 comes to about 437 millionths of a gram. So a pack-a-day smoker—more than 50 percent of the Pope study population considering then-current and former smokers—inhaled 659 times more PM2.5 than was measured by the EPA monitors. So for at least one-half of the Pope study subjects, outdoor air was nowhere close to a significant source of PM2.5.

When it came to secondhand smoke, Pope study subjects inhaled, on average, an estimated 3.2 hours worth of secondhand smoke per day. While exposure to PM2.5 from secondhand smoke is considerably less than from smoking, secondhand smoke exposure to PM2.5 is still more than enough to blow away the Pope study assumption that EPA air quality monitoring is a reasonable or meaningful estimate of exposure to PM2.5.

Smoking in closed cars can expose occupants to concentrations of PM2.5 more than 700 times greater than the average PM2.5 than assumed in the Pope study.[12] Each hour in a restaurant or bar where smoking is allowed may result in an amount of PM2.5 inhaled that exceeds a full day's worth of Pope study exposures.

But that's still not the end of the problems with the Pope study.

When doing epidemiologic studies where you are looking to link an exposure with a disease, you must also consider and rule out other potential risk factors for the disease. For example, if you want to link air pollution with death, you must rule out other competing health, lifestyle, economic and occupational risk factors for death. While this may sound simple, it's not. Without detailed medical evaluation on an individual basis, it's virtually impossible.

The Pope researchers claimed to have used statistical techniques to rule out age, sex, race, smoking, secondhand smoking, body weight, alcohol consumption, education level and occupation as competing or confounding risk factors for death. While it is disputable whether one can simply wave a statistical magic wand over data to eliminate competing risk factors for death, the data on those risk factors would at least need to be high quality data. The Pope study data falls far short on both marks.

The American Cancer Society initially assembled the health, lifestyle, economic and occupational data for the 295,223 adults in the Pope study population. While that may sound impressive, it falls apart upon close inspection. The American Cancer Society assembled the data by asking some 70,000 volunteers to go query their relatives, friends and neighbors about how much they smoked, drank, weighed and the like.

Data collection by 70,000 untrained laymen asking arbitrarily selected people embarrassing questions is not scientific. Such responses are just as likely to produce intentionally wrong as unintentionally wrong responses. And none of the responses are validated or verified in any sort of meaningful way. "Hey Aunt Mary, how many martinis do you usually consume every night?" multiplied by 70,000 is not likely to produce anything in the way of useful information. It was clear that the Pope study was a scientific failure—but the EPA embraced it all the same.

The EPA's other pillar for its proposed PM2.5 rule, the Harvard Six-City study, was conducted with similarly flawed data. It was another case of assumed and misleading exposure data coupled with unverified personal health data that were statistically massaged to produce an exceedingly weak statistical correlation.

So it was no surprise there was skepticism of the data and studies that the EPA relied on for its PM2.5 proposal.

CHAPTER 4

Secret Science

We all know that reports and claims are not true simply because they are in print. What many don't realize, however, is that the same holds for scientific studies. Just because a study has been published in a journal, doesn't mean that its results and the conclusions drawn from them are valid.

While scientific studies typically undergo so-called "peer review" prior to publication, the unfortunate reality is that peer review often amounts to little more than proofreading by sympathetic colleagues. There are no professional, full-time peer reviewers. Being a reviewer for a journal is mostly honorific in nature. They are not highly compensated, if at all, for their work. They generally don't get (or request) access to the data and methodology used in studies. Reviewers typically only have time enough to read through studies and catch obvious errors. Given the collegial nature of scientists, peer review may often be thought of as "pal" review. This unfortunate proofreading exercise risks turning into mere rubberstamping if there are political, financial, or other relationships among the researchers, reviewers and journal staff.

Not to belabor the problems of journal peer review, but it is not really an inherent, necessary or even an important part of the scientific method at all. Simply described, the way that the scientific method works is that a scientist develops an idea or hypothesis (for example, air pollution kills people), collects and analyzes data that he thinks adequately test his hypothesis, publishes the results and then makes his data and methods available to other independent scientists who seek to verify his results by trying to replicate them. This effort at replication is a hallmark of the scientific method. If the results can be replicated, then some confidence can possibly be had in them.

So a mere claim of peer review isn't meaningful in and of itself. But this fact is often lost on journalists, politicians, the public and the media. Purveyors of junk science can easily and often do exploit this.

When the EPA proposed its standards for PM2.5, the agency audaciously claimed that its PM2.5 research, like the Pope and Harvard Six-City studies, had been "intensively peer reviewed."[13] But as previously described, the two studies were fatally flawed. So organizations independent of the EPA asked the agency for the data used in the Harvard Six-City and Pope studies so they could examine them and try to replicate the studies' findings.

The requests began in 1994, two years prior to the EPA's PM2.5 proposal, by none other than the EPA's own group of independent science advisers called the Clean Air Science Advisory Committee (CASAC).[14] The group wrote EPA Administrator Carol Browner asking for the "crucial data sets linking exposure to particulate matter and health responses." But CASAC never received the data.

After the EPA proposed its PM2.5 rule, a utility industry trade association filed a Freedom of Information Act (FOIA) request with the agency. But the EPA replied that it didn't have the data. That statement was technically true, but overlooked the fact that the EPA had paid for both the Harvard Six-City and Pope studies to be conducted. One might reasonably think that the EPA would have been able to persuade the researchers to share the data for the limited purposes of replicating the claimed results.

Then in February 1997, Congress questioned the studies' findings. The then-powerful House Commerce Committee Chairman Thomas Bliley (R-Va.) sent what was described as a "sharply worded letter" to Browner requesting the data, noting the agency paid for the research and had a right to the underlying data. "The public must be given an opportunity to review all of these data so that they can be confident that the EPA is basing its decisions on sound science," Bliley wrote.

Browner didn't bother to respond to Committee Chairman Bliley, either. Instead, she delegated the task to a senior staff member who brazenly told the Congressman, "We do not believe . . . there is a useful purpose for EPA to obtain the underlying data." The reply further stated "securing more detail about this information is not necessary as part of the EPA's public health standard-setting process."[15]

That's how the matter was left when EPA finalized its PM2.5 rule in July 1997.[16] Not only had EPA gotten away with promulgating a rule with highly questionable epidemiology but it also did so on the basis of what essentially was secret science. The PM2.5 rule was so extreme that even the Clinton White House and Vice President Al Gore gagged on what EPA was trying to do.

When then-White House Council of Environmental Quality Chairman Katie McGinty suggested that the EPA simply raise the proposed allowable level PM2.5 in outdoor air level 20 percent—that is, from 15 to 18 millionths-of-a-gram per cubic meter, Browner refused. An exasperated McGinty asked, "Who does she think she is, Joan of Arc?"[17] Gore was reportedly "furious" that Browner didn't consult him on the rule.[18]

Congress didn't take Browner's arrogance entirely lying down. On October 19, 1998, poorly constructed provisions were inserted at the last moment into an emergency spending bill directing the White House Office of Management and Budget (OMB) to issue rules requiring that data produced with any federal funding be made available to the public by means of the Freedom of Information Act law.[19] These so-called "data access" rules were eventually issued in 2002.[20]

Unfortunately for the public, Congress did a lousy job of writing the law on which the data access rules were based. In May 2003, the Salt Institute, a trade association of salt producers, requested the

U.S. Department of Health and Human Services (HHS) provide federally-funded data underlying a large clinical study on dietary ways to reduce high blood pressure. HHS rejected the request on the grounds that it neither possessed the data nor were the data funded prior to the effective date of OMB's data access rules.

A subsequent lawsuit by the Salt Institute against HHS for the data failed when a federal appellate court ruled in 2006 that the data access rules did not provide for judicial enforcement.[21] Exactly why government rules and regulations designed to help the public monitor the government are unenforceable is beyond the scope of the present discussion. But it is a worthy point to ponder.

The EPA had constructed an insurmountable wall around the Harvard Six-City and Pope study data. The lack of a judicial enforcement mechanism in the data access law meant that no one could use it to obtain the data. If the FOIA law was tried, the agency could deny a request based on the fact that it did not have actual possession of the data. Researchers at universities possessed the data and they aren't typically subject to complying with FOIA requests. This was license for the EPA to run amok with PM2.5 and other air quality regulations.

CHAPTER 5

Show US the Bodies, EPA

Barack Obama, then a Senator, told the *San Francisco Chronicle* in a now famous January 2008 interview that if he were president, under his administration, "if someone wanted to build a coal-powered plant, they can. It's just that it will bankrupt them because they're going to be charged a huge sum for all that greenhouse gas that's being emitted."[22] That was perhaps the first shot in what has become known as Obama's "war on coal."

Despite a Democrat-controlled Congress, Obama's first foray as president against the coal industry failed. The 2009 Waxman-Markey bill to impose mandatory greenhouse gas emissions reductions via a cap-and-trade system squeaked pass the House of Representatives by a vote of 219-212, with 8 Republicans voting with the Democrat majority. But the Senate version of the bill floundered, as did several subsequent efforts. So Obama turned to the EPA that he controlled and ordered it to begin issuing regulations to implement his policies.

The EPA proposed the first major war-on-coal regulation in August 2010. Called the Cross-State Air Pollution Rule (CSAPR, pronounced "Caspar," like the ghost), the rule was an ostensible effort to prevent emissions from Midwest coal-fired power plants from drifting eastward. These emissions allegedly caused air quality problems in downrange Eastern states. The existence and significance of this claimed phenomenon was controversial. Even if Midwest smokestack emissions did waft easterly, it was not clear that they had any discernible impact as violations of EPA air quality standards in the East were few and far between.

In an analysis of the CSAPR proposal in March 2011, I examined the most recent EPA air monitoring data for the 32 Midwest and Eastern states that were to be subject to CSAPR. The analysis showed that the EPA's daily air quality standard for PM2.5 was violated less than one-tenth of one percent of the time—0.096 percent to be precise—in 2009.[23] The daily air quality standard for ground-level ozone or smog was violated only 1.3 percent of the time in the 32 states. And even those few violations could not be blamed on Midwestern coal plants.

Moreover, just because an EPA standard is violated, that doesn't necessarily mean that anyone's health is in jeopardy. If nothing else, the Clean Air Act requires that EPA air quality standards "protect the public health" with an "adequate margin of safety."[24] So EPA standards, in theory anyway, are more stringent than the science would indicate.

But the EPA claimed that the CSAPR rule, by reducing eastward wafting PM2.5 emissions from coal-fired power plants, would prevent between 13,000 to 34,000 premature deaths annually.[25] The EPA justified this claim, of course, with the Harvard Six-City and Pope studies—but with a twist.

The EPA made the astounding claim that "the credibility of these two studies [had been] further enhanced" because both studies had undergone "extensive reexamination and reanalysis by an independent team of scientific experts commissioned by the Health Effect Institute (HEI)."[26] That sounds impressive unless you know anything about the HEI and its review of the Harvard Six-City and Pope studies.

Though the EPA claimed that the HEI conducted an "extensive reexamination and reanalysis," that is quite different than an effort to replicate the results of the Pope study. The HEI admitted in its reanalysis that it never obtained the original health data or the original air quality data used in the Pope study.[27] How could HEI possibly validate the Pope study without having any of the original data? This can perhaps be explained by the special relationship between the HEI and the EPA.

Although the EPA described the HEI team of scientific experts as "independent," the EPA and the auto industry jointly funded HEI. As the EPA regulates the auto industry, which long ago gave up challenging the EPA, the HEI was essentially an arm of the EPA. (There will be much more to say later about the EPA's financial relationships with its scientific reviewers.)

Oddly enough, the EPA's CSAPR proposal was reassuring. The agency was still relying on the Harvard Six-City and Pope studies. It was at this time the "Show Us the Bodies, EPA" op-ed was published in the Washington Times.[28] It hit a nerve.

Soon after the op-ed, the House Oversight and Government Reform subcommittee held a hearing at which Congressman Dennis Kucinich (D-OH) asked Deputy EPA Administrator Robert Perciasepe about the op-ed:[29]

REP. KUCINICH: On July 20, 2011, the Washington Times *ran an op-ed by Steve Milloy, the publisher of JunkScience. com, titled 'Show Us the Bodies, EPA.' The subtitle reads 'Green Agencies Use Phony Death Statistics to Justify Job Killing Rules.' Quote, unquote. The op-ed described a TV ad run by the Environmental Defense Fund saying, 'The TV ad for this theme features a young girl in a hospital bed, supposedly having an asthma attack. She's wearing a nebulizer, face mask and chest compression device that is rhythmically but disturbingly squeezing the child, giving the appearance that she is in severe respiratory distress, by implication, from air pollution. But like the EPA's 17,000 lives saved statistical fabrication, the ads are fake.'*

Now, Mr. Perciasepe, I'd like to give you a chance to respond to this op-ed. It's apparently aimed at EPA's proposed toxic—air toxic rule. Are EPA's estimated benefits from the proposed rule a statistical fabrication?

MR. PERCIASEPE: They're based on peer-reviewed science. They're not a statistical fabrication and they're—you're not going to see on somebody's death certificate, they died of air pollution. They're going to die of the diseases that air pollution exacerbates and causes premature impacts. Even healthy people are impacted. But people who are more vulnerable, like retired folks, are going to be even more vulnerable to these things. So the impact of the damage on the lungs and the cardiovascular system. So I know you have other witnesses that will go into the science of this in more detail, but these are not fabricated. They're based on peer-reviewed science, both clinical and epidemiological studies.

But as discussed previously, the mere fact that a study was peer-reviewed is not an indicator of its scientific validity. And Perciasepe's speculation about how air pollution might kill people is a far cry from producing a body, which he admitted that the EPA couldn't actually do.

Then Dr. Lynn Goldman, a former Clinton administration EPA official and dean of the George Washington School of Public Health, responded with a letter to the *Washington Times* and a blog post titled "Attn: Steve Milloy—I've Seen the Bodies."[30, 31] Goldman wrote:

Steven Milloy, a commentator for Fox News, recently published a piece in the Washington Times, *attacking the bedrock clean air laws that protect Americans from pollution. In his editorial, 'Doubting the health benefits of cleaner air,' Mr. Milloy claimed that the EPA 'fabricated' statistics that mercury and other air toxics harm people. He demanded: "Show me the bodies."*

I was deeply offended. I know that so many husbands, wives and children can show him the bodies—those of their

loved ones who dropped dead from a heart attack after breath-
ing too much polluted air on a code orange or code red day. I
could only think of the many children admitted to the hospital
for asthma attacks on days when smog levels are sky-high,
children who miss so many days of school that they can't keep
up with their classmates, children who must be on medication
every day to lead anything close to a normal life.

As a research scientist, I know that volumes of medical
science document the harm that air pollution does to the
human body. The scientific community has concluded that air
pollution causes disease and death. I know that people living
in areas with high air pollution concentrations have excessive
heart and lung disease, emergency room visits, hospitalizations
and premature death.

As a pediatrician, I have attended to the children suffering
from asthma attacks. They are too young to stand up to Mr.
Milloy and his industry sponsors, but their developing lungs
count on the protections the nation's clean air laws provide.

That was a dramatic essay, but Goldman's unsubstantiated gen-
eralizations and claims did not "show me a body" or even point me
in the direction of one might be found.

Aside from completing a residency in pediatrics more than 25
years ago, Goldman has been spent much of her career as a bureaucrat
and politico in the California state government and at the EPA,
towing their respective policy lines.[32] If Lynn Goldman's thin gruel
was the best EPA and the enviros could come up with, that was yet
another pretty good indicator that, in fact, there were no
bodies to be found.

The executive director of the Institute for Policy Integrity at New
York University School of Law, Michael A Livermore also took aim:

Milloy makes a specific request to see 'bodies,' and sadly, that
is easy enough to show him . . . If Milloy is actually interested

*in looking for the 'bodies,' he should simply examine the
peer-reviewed studies that back up the EPA's analysis.*

But the studies had already been examined.

It was surprising that the EPA's allies even bothered to respond
to "Show Us the Bodies." The EPA and its allies typically ignore
critics in the expectation that they will simply go away. Pretending
critics don't exist has been an effective strategy for decades. But for
some reason, not this time. The Kucinich-Perciasepe exchange, in
particular, sounded quite a bit like one of the oft-scripted exchanges
one hears during congressional hearings between like-minded
Members of Congress and witnesses.

One other response of note to "Show Us the Bodies, EPA" came
from an official of the mega-green group Environmental Defense
Fund. Amid a spirited debate in the JunkScience.com comments,
Sam Parry challenged back:[33]

> *I just wish someone on here—anyone—would provide one
> single link to a peer-reviewed scientific study denying that
> current air pollution levels contribute to the premature deaths
> of tens of thousands of Americans per year. Is that really
> too much to ask?*

"One single link"? That was all? No problem. There was a 2005
study published in the journal Inhalation Toxicology by UCLA
epidemiologist James E. Enstrom. In the study, Enstrom looked to
see if there was a correlation between $PM_{2.5}$ and death in a group
49,975 elderly Californians, with a mean age of 65 years as of 1973.[34]

The data ran through the year 2002, by which time 39,846 of
the study subjects had died. From his analysis, Enstrom concluded that:

> *These epidemiologic results do not support a current relationship
> between [$PM_{2.5}$] and [death] in elderly Californians.*

Thus satisfying the Environmental Defense Fund's challenge, Parry responded:

Okay, now we're talking. Science. At last. Thank you for finally posting an actual scientific paper.
It does appear that this study finds no link between PM2.5 and the mortality rate of elderly Californians . . .
I congratulate you for finding one scientific study out of hundreds that does cast some doubt on the link between PM2.5 and mortality in 11 counties in California.
As for the bodies, look at the abundance of science on air pollution and mortality. The bodies are there. I think even Enstrom would agree.

So not surprisingly, satisfying Parry's challenge wasn't enough. After all, there were "hundreds" of studies with contrary results, he claimed—although even the EPA had boiled them down to two, the Harvard Six City and Pope studies.

But for the sake of argument, let's allow for the moment Parry's claim that "hundreds" of studies contradicting Enstrom's existed. Enstrom's study would still be sufficient to call the validity of the hundreds into question.

If there existed a single circumstance where the law of gravity didn't hold true, it wouldn't be called a law or esteemed as such by scientists. Similarly, if PM2.5 in outdoor air killed people, then it kills people everywhere all the time and it would be unlikely that Enstrom had found the one group of almost 50,000 elderly people where that is not the case.

So far "Show Us the Bodies, EPA" had turned out to be a wonderful exercise in eliciting the vapidity of the EPA's PM2.5 claims.

CHAPTER 6

It Just Kills You

About six weeks after the hub-bub over "Show Us the Bodies, EPA" died down, the report appeared about the EPA's researchers exposing the sick and overweight 58-year-old woman to a very high level of PM2.5. This was the exposure that allegedly produced an irregular heartbeat or arrhythmia requiring emergency hospitalization of the woman.[35]

At first glance, the report was perplexing. The woman hadn't died. Still it was necessary to go through the report and look for ways to debunk the EPA researchers' conclusion that the case "supports a causal relationship between" exposure to PM2.5 and heart disease.

The woman seemed to be a physical wreck. She was 58-years-old, 5 feet 8 inches tall and weighed 230 pounds. Her medical history indicated that she had a personal medical history of stage 1 hypertension, pre-mature atrial contractions, osteoarthritis, gall bladder removal, knee replacement and hernia repair. And she had a family history of heart disease—as mentioned previously, her father suffered a fatal heart attack at age 57.

The EPA had exposed her to an amount of PM2.5 never inhaled anywhere outdoors under typical conditions in the U.S. That level, 112 millionths-of-a-gram per cubic meter of air, was more than three times greater than the EPA's 24-hour standard for PM2.5 in outdoor air, 35 millionths-of-a-gram per cubic meter of air.[36]

33

As determined earlier, the 35 millionths-of-a-gram standard was only surpassed roughly 0.33 percent of the time in the eastern U.S. from 2007 to 2009.

So the initial review indicated that the case report was about a study subject who was pre-disposed-to-atrial-fibrillation and who was made to inhale far more PM2.5 than virtually ever exists in outdoor air. She experienced a temporary and not uncommon medical event that could have multiple potential causes—none of which had anything to do with the quality of outdoor air.

Then an emergency room physician colleague with whom the study had been shared pointed out a jaw-dropping paragraph in the study:

> *Approximately six weeks [after the experiment and hospitalization, the 58-year-old study subject] underwent electrophysiology study, which did not provoke atrial fibrillation or significant atrial ectopy. The study did indicate a reentrant circuit of the cavotricuspid isthmus which was ablated to prevent potential future episodes of atrial flutter.*

The translation is that the 58-year-old woman went back for follow-up cardiac testing at which time doctors discovered she had a pre-existing aberrant nerve pathway in her heart muscle. Doctors then essentially electrocuted the pathway so that it would not cause further heart problems—like the one she experienced during the EPA experiment—in the future.

Case reports of one or a few patients are anecdotal in nature and so are not considered to be scientific. A sample size of one is a sample of nothing that can be generalized to a scientific principle. What happened to the 58-year-old woman is a good example of why that is so. But the appalling aspect here is that the EPA researchers affirmatively tried to present this case report as evidence supporting the agency's claim that PM2.5 can kill people.

Not only should the EPA researchers have known better than to pretend the case of the 58-year-old woman was caused by PM2.5, the editors of the journal, Environmental Health Perspectives, where the report was published, should have know better. If the case report were worthy of publication at all, possibly a cardiology, emergency medicine or other medical journal would have been appropriate. But a journal supposedly spotlighting environmental science research? What kind of peer review did the case report undergo? Any? Or was it just one of those rubberstamp-as-peer-reviewed jobs? There will be more on this point later.

Though the EPA's effort to serve up a body failed, there were lingering questions surrounding this case study that were odd. [37]

How did the EPA researchers get this 58-year-old woman to inhale massive amounts of PM2.5 in the first place? What was the arrangement? Did she just happen to wander into an EPA laboratory? Were there others so exposed? What, if anything, happened to them? Do we only get to hear about the one result that could possibly be twisted to fit the EPA's agenda? To get the answers, a request to the EPA for the results of related experiments was submitted under the Freedom of Information Act.

A week later on September 22, 2011, then-EPA Administrator Lisa Jackson testified before a subcommittee of the House Energy and Commerce Committee when she engaged in the following astounding colloquy with Rep. Edward Markey (D-Mass.) about PM2.5 (here, simply referred to as "particulate matter"): [38]

Mr. Markey: Cumulatively, what are the benefits of cleaning up particulate matter? Does that help or hurt our efforts to battle cancer, to battle the impact that it has upon the health of people in our country?

Ms. Jackson: Particulate matter causes premature deaths. It doesn't make you sick. It is directly causal to dying sooner than you should. So the impacts of delaying efforts, cost-effective

*efforts, I might add, to address particulate matter are more
people dying sooner than they should.*

This was jaw-dropping testimony. EPA Administrator Jackson
essentially likened PM2.5—remember this is just common dust and
soot found in everyday air—to a bullet to the head, a stab to the
heart and the downing of cyanide, all of which don't make you sick
but simply kill you. It's almost enough to make you think twice
about breathing.

But there was more astounding testimony to come:

*Mr. Markey: How would you compare it to the fight against
cancer, reducing particulate matter?*

*Ms. Jackson: Yes, I was briefed not long ago. If we could reduce
particulate matter to healthy levels, it would have the same
impact as finding a cure for cancer in our country.*

Mr. Markey: Can you say that sentence one more time?

*Ms. Jackson: Yes, sir. If we could reduce particulate matter to
levels that are healthy, we would have an identical impact to
finding a cure for cancer.*

The notion that reducing PM2.5 was equivalent to curing cancer
was incredible. In 2011, about 2.5 million people died in the U.S.[39]
Of these deaths, about 570,000, or 23 percent, were from cancer.[40]
So EPA Administrator Jackson had just told Congress that PM2.5
was the cause of almost one in four deaths in America.

Yet no one had or could identify a single one.

CHAPTER 7

The EPA's Golden Goose

A couple months later in November 2011, the EPA responded to the Freedom of Information Act request about whether there were any other people in addition to the 58-year-old woman who the EPA had exposed to PM2.5.[41] It was yet another jaw-dropping response.

Enclosed with the letter was a spreadsheet containing the dates, study-coded subject identifiers, times, PM2.5 exposure levels and clinical health effects observed for 41 people who the EPA had somehow wrangled into inhaling PM2.5 from January 2010 to June 2011. Each of the 41 were apparently placed in some sort of chamber and made to inhale varying amounts of PM2.5 for a period of up to two hours. It was the exposure levels—in relation to the EPA's own regulatory standards—that were astounding.

The study subjects were exposed to a range of PM2.5 from 41 millionths-of-a-gram per cubic meter of air to 750 millionths-of-a-gram per cubic meter of air. Keeping in mind that outdoor air with PM2.5 that exceeds 35 millionths-of-a-gram per hour on a 24-hour basis violates EPA regulations, the EPA had apparently intentionally exposed people to levels of PM2.5 that exceeded the target hourly standard by as much as 21 times for up to 2 hours at a time!

But just two months earlier, EPA Administrator Jackson testified to Congress that PM2.5 doesn't make you sick, it kills you. She also said that about one in four deaths in the U.S. was caused by PM2.5

in outdoor air—despite the fact that outdoor air complies with the EPA's PM2.5 standard 99.9 percent of the time, according to the analysis of the EPA's Cross-State Air Pollution Rule.

The spreadsheet indicated that 2 of the 41 study subjects experienced "clinical effects," defined as requiring medical follow-up or referral to a physician. One study subject was the 58-year-old woman previously discussed. The other study subject reportedly experienced a "short episode of elevated heart rate during exposure." Though the individual denied having any symptoms, the EPA provided her copies of the electrocardiogram and referred her to a physician. There was no note of the results of any follow-up that may have occurred.

At about the same time as these results came to light, the EPA came out with yet another war-on-coal rule based on PM2.5.

The EPA finalized its Mercury Air Transport Standard (MATS) rule in December 2011. Although the rule nominally dealt with emissions of mercury from coal-fired power plants, it was really a rule that actually relied on the premise that PM2.5 killed thousands of people every year.

At this point, we need to discuss how the EPA comes up with something called "cost-benefit analysis," a calculation made to show how the estimated societal benefits of a rule match up with its estimated costs.

When it comes to substances in the air like PM2.5, the Clean Air Act legally bars the EPA from considering costs when setting air quality standards. The Supreme Court has held that the EPA can only set air quality standards based on scientific determinations that provide an adequate margin of safety so as to protect the public health.[42] So why does the EPA even bother to calculate costs and benefits for PM2.5?

Almost as soon as regulatory agencies like the EPA became a force to be reckoned with in the late-1960 and 1970s, it had become clear that some restraints were needed to prevent the economy from being regulated into oblivion for no purpose. The administrations of Presidents Nixon, Ford and Carter wrestled with various ways to ensure that regulations produced actual benefits and that such benefits were worthwhile considering the costs of regulation.[43] Then President Reagan developed a practice for evaluating regulations. Reagan's so-called "cost-benefit analysis" has survived to this day, at least in concept.

President Reagan issued Executive Order 12291 in February 1981, directing federal agencies like EPA to conduct cost-benefit analyses on "major" regulations, that is those having an economic impact of $100 million or more.[44] Most importantly, Executive Order 12291 directed agencies to not take regulatory action "unless the potential benefits to society for the regulation outweigh the potential costs to society." Although Executive Order 12291 was not a law and could not be legally enforced by anyone, it was administration policy that was enforced politically by the regulatory watchdogs in the Office of Information and Regulatory Affairs (OIRA) at the White House Office of Management and Budget.

During the Reagan and George H.W. Bush administrations, OIRA was empowered to enforce cost-benefit discipline on the EPA and other regulatory agencies. Before rules could be proposed and then finalized, OIRA review was undertaken. And if the bean counters at OIRA thought that a rule's costs were greater than its benefits, it was likely going nowhere but back to the agency's drawing board. Executive Order 12291 was not a foolproof system but it did stop, or slow, a great deal of regulatory expansion, especially at the EPA.

In September 1993, then-President Clinton cancelled Executive Order 12291 and replaced it with his own Executive Order 12866, which only required that "the benefits of the intended regulation justify its costs"—a much more relaxed standard than Executive Order 12291's requirement that benefits exceed costs.[45] This signaled a shift of power from the defanged OIRA back to the regulatory agencies like the Carol Browner-powered EPA. A notable result of this shift was the 1996 PM2.5 standards that the EPA likely never would have gotten past the Reagan-Bush era OIRA.

Although the EPA had acquired the political muscle to overcome, if not disregard OIRA, the notion of cost-benefit analysis had become a fixed idea in the regulatory system. Congress and the public had come to expect that regulations would produce benefits that exceeded their costs. The Clinton EPA's challenge was to figure out how to game the cost-benefits analysis for its PM2.5 rules.

When EPA proposed its first PM2.5 rule in 1997, it estimated the costs of compliance with the rule to be about $6 billion per year.[46] At 60 times greater than the $100 million threshold established by President Reagan for a "major regulation," $6 billion was a great deal of money back then. Nevertheless, it was a lowball figure as even President Clinton's Council of Economic Advisers pegged the proposal's costs as 10 times higher at $60 billion.[47] But the agency proceeded to estimate the benefits of the rule approached in excess of $100 billion per year, putting even the $60 billion cost estimate in the shade. So how did the EPA make this astounding calculation?

Ostensibly, the calculation was pretty straightforward. Recall that the EPA estimated in 1996 its PM2.5 rule would prevent 20,000 premature deaths per year. As the EPA valued in 1997 each life saved at about $5 million, 20,000-lives-saved-per-year multiplied by $5 million-per-life-saved equals $100 billion per year. But past the simple multiplication, how does one value something for which there is no price, such as a human life?

Economists have a methodology called "contingent valuation" that fabricates values virtually out of the imaginations of randomly selected and surveyed people. The key concept in contingent valuation is a notion called "willingness-to-pay." How much is someone willing to pay for whatever the thing is that has no market price. In the case of PM2.5, the question might be posed as, "How much are you willing to pay to not die prematurely?" Keep in mind, no one is asking you to fork over actual money. It's a game of imagination in which you are asked how much would you be willing to pay?

As economists feel that there is apparently little point in asking people how much would they pay to save their own lives, they phrase the question in a way that they think respondents are less likely to overvalue themselves. So here's the question relied on by the EPA's economists: How much would you be willing to pay to reduce your risk of premature death by one-in-one hundred thousandth (1 in 100,000)?

"Premature death" means dying before you otherwise would. This could mean decades or even days, as in dying Tuesday instead of Wednesday. So let's say the odds of you dying on tomorrow were 50 percent. How much would you pay to reduce that chance to 49.999 percent?

Believe it or not, people apparently try to answer such questions. Based on the contingent valuation surveys available in 1996, those surveyed put a value on reducing their chance of premature death by 1-in-100,000 at about $50. To value an entire life, then, EPA multiplied this $50 by 100,000 and—voila—a life saved is worth $5 million. Or at least it was in 1997. Since then, EPA has calculated that we humans are even more valuable and will become even more so in the future. As of 2006, the value of a life saved was $7.4 million. By 2020, it will rise to about $9 million, according to the EPA.[48]

Now that you have some idea of how the EPA estimates the benefits of its PM2.5 rules, let's get back to the agency's real-life application of these imaginary numbers.

Despite the name of the MATS rule, controlling mercury emissions from coal plants did not offer much in the way of tangible societal benefits. When the EPA tried to value the potential public health benefits from the rule, it could only estimate a hypothetical $6 million worth. This obviously paled in comparison with rule's estimated $11 billion in far-more-tangible costs.

But the EPA knew that the MATS rule would be so expensive that many coal plants would simply be shut down by their electric utility owners rather than the owners investing in any additional expensive emissions control equipment. The shuttering of these plants would then eliminate their emissions that, in turn, would further reduce PM2.5 in outdoor air.

The EPA then estimated that by reducing PM2.5, albeit indirectly, as many as 11,000 lives would be saved every year—with every life worth $9 million or so, the EPA estimated the benefits of the rule to be worth as much as $90 billion per year. And since $90 billion in benefits is a lot more than $11 billion in costs, EPA had solved its cost-benefit problem. Never mind that the $90 billion in costs were imaginary in nature while the $11 billion costs were actual in nature. Only a few people actually knew enough about that fact to dispute it in any intelligent manner and, for a variety of reasons, those people were effectively silenced.

In 2011, EPA estimated that its two war-on-coal rules, the ear-lier-issued Cross-State Air Pollution Rule and the MATS rule, would prevent up to 46,000 premature deaths annually. Saving these lives, according to EPA, would provide estimated economic benefits amounting to a staggering $380 billion per year.[49]

To put this claim in perspective, consider that the U.S. Gross Domestic Product (GDP) for 2014—that is, the value of the goods and services by the American economy—is about $17 trillion. EPA claims that its two rules will provide health benefits worth about 2.2 percent of the entire economy.

In an even more grandiose assessment of its regulations, the EPA estimates that by 2020, its implementation of the Clean Air Act will provide economic benefits worth $2 trillion per year. Of this amount $1.7 trillion will come from preventing 230,000 deaths through reductions of outdoor PM2.5.[50] If the U.S. GDP were to be on the order of, say, $22 trillion by 2020, then EPA's PM2.5 rules would be worth about 9 percent of our economy.

In EPA's mind, it is a goose that lays golden regulations.

CHAPTER 8

Who Is the EPA Lying To?

Four months after receiving the EPA's response to my FOIA request regarding the agency's PM2.5 experiment on the 58-year-old woman, a framework for working the issue finally formed. In order to fully understand and appreciate the purpose of the activity covered in the next few chapters pertaining to EPA's human experiments, a brief overview is in order.

Given that EPA had declared any inhalation of PM2.5 could be lethal, the EPA had no business conducting experiments on humans with PM2.5. In fact, such experiments would be, by their very nature unethical and illegal, according to federal and state laws and regulations. But the EPA was conducting them anyway, which certainly suggests that the agency knew PM2.5 wouldn't actually kill anyone. So why conduct the experiments?

The EPA was conducting the experiments because it was desperate to give some biological or medical support to its epidemiologic studies, which are merely statistical in nature. What the EPA hoped to do was to expose its human guinea pigs to high levels of PM2.5 in hopes of observing some sort of effect that the EPA could then extrapolate to a serious health effect or even death.

Pursuing the EPA and its human experiments with PM2.5 was then a means of exposing the fact that the EPA knew that PM2.5 didn't actually kill anyone. That fact would be the only thing that stood between the EPA and the commission of multiple felonies. So in order to pursue this point, I adopted the posture of taking the EPA's word and accepting the EPA's PM2.5 claims at face value. So if it seems odd that I'm asserting that EPA's PM2.5 claims are true, remember that my sole purpose is to flush out of EPA an admission that it knows PM2.5 is, in fact, not dangerous or lethal.

So on with the story.

On April 24, 2012, I published an op-ed in the *Washington Times* that posed the following question:[51]

> *Which do you find more shocking: that the Environmental Protection Agency conducts experiments on humans that its own risk assessments would deem potentially lethal, or that it hides the results of those experiments from Congress and the public because they debunk those very same risk assessments?*

The thrust of the piece was pretty straightforward. For the past 15 years, EPA had told the public and had imposed onerous air quality regulations on the basis that PM2.5 killed people. PM2.5 was so deadly that EPA deemed localities in violation of the Clean Air Act if PM2.5 levels in the air exceeded 35 millionths-of-a-gram per cubic meter of air per hour averaged on a daily basis. And here was the EPA intentionally exposing people to up to 21 times more PM2.5 than the target standard for two hours at a time. EPA Administrator Lisa Jackson had testified before Congress that PM2.5 didn't make people sick, it killed them. But in the data the EPA had given me, no one died or even experienced a clinical health effect that could be reasonably attributed to PM2.5.

I concluded by asking:

> *In light of the EPA's own [claims about the lethality of PM2.5], how far is the agency's conduct from the horrific experiments conducted by the Nazi concentration camp doctor Josef Mengele*

*and the Tuskegee syphilis experiments? What should we make
of the agency hiding its results from the public and Congress?*

Comparing EPA's PM2.5 experiments to human experiment
horrors of the past may seem extreme—but then, again, maybe not.
EPA had repeatedly made strongly worded claims about the absolute
lethality of PM2.5.

The history of scientific experiments on humans is a long and
sordid one. Recall EPA Administrator Jackson told Congress in
September 2011: "Particulate matter causes premature deaths. It
doesn't make you sick. It is directly causal to dying sooner than you
should." Even if you are skeptical of Jackson's claim, pretend it is
true for the next few moments.

In 1932, the U.S. Public Health Service began the "Tuskegee
Study of Untreated Syphilis in the Negro Male."[52] Six hundred poor
rural black men were enrolled in the study, 399 of which had contracted syphilis. The men had no idea why they were enrolled. They
were simply told that they had "bad blood." In exchange for their
participation in the study they would be treated for their "bad blood,"
receive free medical exams, free meals and burial insurance. The
purpose of the study, concealed from these poor men, was to observe
the natural progression of untreated syphilis—and did not include
any sort of actual medical treatment for their "bad blood."

About 10 years after the abuse of the Tuskegee men began, an
entirely new set of inhumane scientific experiments started in Nazi
Germany on concentration camp prisoners. Prisoners were frozen,
poisoned, mutilated, tortured, sterilized and burned—all to help
the Nazi war machine. Some experiments were undertaken to advance
Nazi race theory and some were undertaken to advance twisted
personal interests, such as Josef Mengele's horrific experiments on twins.

After the war, accountability for these horrors was visited on
many of those responsible for them. Sixteen of the 23 physicians
tried at the Nuremburg war crimes tribunal during what is known

as the "Doctors Trial" were hanged. As part of the verdict, the tribunal issued its views on human experimentation.

The "Nuremberg Code" contained 10 principles for researchers wishing to experiment on humans that are summarized as follows:

1. *Researchers must disclose risks to study subjects who, in turn, must then provide voluntary consent before participating in an experiment.*

2. *Experiments should produce useful results that cannot be obtained by other means.*

3. *Experiments should be designed and based on the results of animal experimentation and knowledge of the natural history of the disease so that the anticipated results will justify the performance of the experiment.*

4. *Experiments should avoid unnecessary physical and mental suffering and injury.*

5. *No experiment should be conducted where there is a prior reason to believe that death or disabling injury will occur.*

6. *The degree of risk to be taken should never exceed that determined by the humanitarian importance of the problem to be solved by the experiment.*

7. *Proper preparations should be made and adequate facilities provided to protect the experimental subject against even remote possibilities of injury, disability, or death.*

8. *Experiments should be conducted by scientifically qualified persons.*

9. *Human subjects are free to end their participation in an experiment.*

10. *Scientists are obligated to end experiments if there is cause to believe that a continuation of the experiment is likely to result in injury, disability, or death to the experimental subject.*

Remember that you were asked to pretend that what EPA claimed about PM2.5 was true. Now would be a good time to do that. Re-read principle No. 5, for example.

But even as the Nuremberg Code was issued and Nazi doctors were executed for their crimes against humanity, not everyone was paying attention. The U.S. Public Health Service doctors, for example, simply carried on with their study of untreated syphilis in poor black men who were purposefully kept in the dark about their condition.

The Tuskegee experiment didn't end until July 1972 when a whistleblower took the story to the media. But by then, many of the men had already died and/or had communicated their syphilis to their wives and, through their wives, to their children. None of the Tuskegee scientists were put on trial or even disciplined. The U.S. Government instead settled with the men and their survivors out-of-court for $10 million and lifetime free medical care.

Although the Nazi human experimentation crimes never directly led to a single law or regulation governing the protection of human subjects in scientific experiments, the Tuskegee horrors did—sort of.

Two years after news of the Tuskegee syphilis experiments broke, the National Research Act of 1974 was enacted. The law set no standards governing the protection of humans in scientific research. It instead called for a commission to study the matter. Five years later, the commission produced a document called the Belmont Report, which laid out some basic principles for the protection of human subjects involved in scientific research.

Between 1981 and 1991, the principles of the Belmont Report were incorporated into federal regulations known as the "Common Rule."[53] The EPA began implementing the principles of the Belmont Report through an internal policy called EPA Order 1000.17. The EPA adopted the Common Rule in 1991 and has since updated both EPA Order 1000.17 and the Common Rule to serve its own purposes.

CHAPTER 9

Circling the Wagons

The EPA's website describes its Human Studies Review Board as a "federal advisory committee that provides advice, information and recommendations on issues of human subjects research." It seemed like a reasonable place to start pursuing the issue of EPA researchers testing the supposedly lethal PM2.5 on people.

So on the same day the Washington Times ran the op-ed about the EPA human experiments, I emailed Dr. Sean Philpot, director of the bioethics program at the Mount Sinai School of Medicine and the chairman of EPA's Human Studies Review Board. Philpot received a copy of the article and was asked whether the Human Studies Review Board had reviewed the EPA's PM2.5 experiments. Surprisingly, he responded.

Philpot indicated that he had already seen the article and had shared it with his colleagues on the Board.[54] Then he added,

> *We did not review these studies . . . the authority of the Human Studies Research Board extends only to third-party conducted research submitted to or used by the Agency for regulatory decision making purposes. The experiments were conducted in-house and not sponsored by a third party.*

So, ironically, the EPA had a Human Studies Research Board that had no jurisdiction over human studies that the agency itself was conducting. A re-read of the case report of the 58-year-old woman revealed that it was the University of North Carolina School of Medicine Committee on the Protection of the Rights of Human Subjects that was responsible for approving the experiments.

I went back to ask Philpot to inquire how a third party got involved in the human experiments. Philpot responded by saying he didn't know much about the experiments or about the University of North Carolina's involvement. But he did direct me to one Warren Lux, who Philpot curiously referred to as the "former (outgoing?)" director of the EPA's Program in Human Research Ethics. It was odd that Philpot, as chairman of the EPA's Human Studies Research Board, had no idea whether Lux, EPA's director of human research ethics, was even on the job. Lux was emailed on April 25, 2011. On May 2, I received the only response I would ever get from him, despite repeated efforts.

In response to the question about the University of North Carolina's involvement, Lux explained that the EPA's Human Studies Research Board was merely an external advisory committee chartered under federal law to advise the EPA on human pesticide research submitted to the EPA in support of pesticide registration applications.[55] So why did Philpot, the chair of the Human Studies Research Board, not know about the University of North Carolina's involvement?

Lux further explained that the EPA Human Studies Facility was located on the University of North Carolina School of Medicine campus and that the EPA had contracted with the university to act as the Common Rule-required Institutional Review Board (IRB) for the agency's human experiments. So the EPA had cleverly outsourced, for a fee, the management and responsibility for its human experiments to the University of North Carolina. The EPA's own staff could do the research it wanted while the university shield would enable and, if necessary, act as a sort of shield for that work. That is, the EPA could always point to an ostensibly independent party as having approved the experiments.

But the insertion of a third party doesn't in any way release the EPA from responsibility of its human experiments. The EPA's Order 1000.17 requires that:[56]

> *All human subject research studies supported by EPA must either be approved or be determined to be exempt research by the EPA Human Subjects Research Review Official before any contract [or] grant . . . involving EPA support of such studies is awarded or entered into. All human research studies conducted by EPA also must be approved or determined to be exempt by the Review Official before work can start.*

So I asked Lux on the same day, who was the "Review Official" mentioned in EPA Order 1000.17 and requested a copy of the EPA's agreement with the University of North Carolina. Despite repeated effort, Lux never again responded.

Five months later, amid publicity about the EPA's human testing program, the following email appeared in my inbox.[57] It was from a source that wished at the time to remain anonymous. The email read:

> *I saw the recent article related to the EPA human subjects testing. I'm a former EPA contractor and I think there are some important questions that you aren't yet asking. The EPA's Program in Human Research Ethics is nonexistent. Literally. It's sole professional staff member resigned earlier this year because both the EPA Administrator and the Associate Administrator for Research and Development refused to acknowledge the need for a credible oversight program necessary for the type of research the EPA conducts. There is a long paper trail between the former research ethics official (Dr. Warren Lux) and Administrator Jackson and Associate Administrator Anastas outlining the deficiencies in the EPA's program for protecting human subjects. The research ethics official eventually*

resigned out of frustration at the lack of action and the position has remained vacant since then. There have been a series of people acting in this position, but none of them have any background in bioethics. The program never had any professional staff and was never a credible program on par with other grant issuing agencies like NIH. Other than whether the experiments in question are unethical, a larger question is whether the EPA should be conducting human subjects research at all without an oversight program. I believe a FOIA request of documents related to recommendations and documentation of deficiencies from the Human Subjects Research Review Official (Dr. Warren Lux, now resigned) to Administrator Jackson and Associate Administrator Anastas related to the Program in Human Research Ethics would bear some fruit on a much larger issue.

This email explained the disappearance of Lux and possibly even his apparent desire to remain out of the spotlight on this issue.

Meanwhile, the day before Lux responded to my email, one of the EPA researchers involved in the report of the 58-year-old woman had responded to the Tuskegee op-ed with a letter published in the *Washington Times*. In defense of EPA's human testing, Wayne E. Cascio, director of the EPA's Environmental Public Health Division wrote:[58]

Steve Milloy's recent Op-Ed ('Did Obama's EPA relaunch Tuskegee experiments?' Commentary, April 25) makes allegations about critical scientific research into how air pollution might contribute to abnormal heart rhythms.

The Environmental Protection Agency's (EPA) research into the health impacts of air pollution has helped to build healthier communities, provide new technology and develop new solutions to protect and manage air quality. In the case of research into fine-particle pollution, more than 50 clinical studies over the past decade involving human volunteers have been published by scientists from the EPA, many U.S. universities and medical centers. These describe cardiac effects in humans exposed to this harmful pollution.

The EPA follows the Common Rule, which requires the ethical review and oversight of human research by an independent Institutional Review Board (IRB) to ensure that any risks to study volunteers are minimized and justified. The EPA follows strict human safety protocols for all of its studies and these protocols are reviewed and approved by the IRB before any human study is conducted. Precautions are taken throughout the volunteer's participation to ensure his safety. In the case of the EPA's research on particle pollution, scientists studied biological changes that carry no or minimal risk while providing evidence for the reasons that particle pollution can lead to serious health problems.

The EPA has established health-based standards for fine-particulate matter and these protect the public from serious health problems, including aggravated asthma, increased hospital admissions, heart attacks and premature death. Individuals particularly sensitive to fine-particle exposure include people with heart or lung disease, older adults and children.

In the United States, a heart attack occurs every 34 seconds and more than 2,200 people die of cardiovascular disease each day. It is estimated that tens of thousands of premature deaths and nonfatal heart attacks are triggered by air pollution and this emphasizes the importance of research in this field. The health scientists and staff at the EPA are privileged to provide safe, ethical, unbiased and state-of-the-art inhalation science in support of the Clean Air Act as we work to define and understand the risks of air pollution to the American people.

Cascio's letter did everything possible to characterize the EPA's experiments as safe and ethical, yet he failed to address the question actually leveled in the *Washington Times* op-ed: Did EPA conduct unethical scientific experiments on people or has it been exaggerating the dangers of PM2.5? He approached the question with this statement:

> *In the case of the EPA's research on particle pollution, scientists* <u>*studied biological changes that carry no or minimal risk*</u> *while providing evidence for the reasons that particle pollution can lead to serious health problems.* [Emphasis added]

But Cascio's claim of the experiments carrying "no or minimal risk" did not at all square with EPA Administrator Lisa Jackson's September 2011 Congressional testimony that,

> *Particulate matter causes premature deaths. It doesn't make you sick.*

If PM2.5 just killed people and didn't make them sick, how could the experiments possibly be "safe" and "ethical" as Cascio claimed? Obviously, they could not be.

CHAPTER 10

A Problem 'Too Obvious to Require Discussion'

Two weeks after the EPA's response appeared in the *Washington Times*, I wrote to the EPA Inspector General Arthur Elkins asking for an investigation into what was termed EPA's "illegal human experimentation."[59] Using the facts available at the time, a strong case was presented against the agency's human experiments involving PM2.5.

That case began with an outline of the applicable rules, including the federal Common Rule and EPA Order 1000.17. Under the Common Rule, risks to health and safety in experiments involving humans must be reasonable in relation to the anticipated benefits of the experiment and they must not be unnecessary. Unless experiments involve only "minimal risk," researchers must obtain informed consent from the human study subjects. "Minimal risk" means that the probability of harm in the research is not greater than that ordinarily encountered in daily life. Informed consent means that the study subjects have been informed of any reasonably foreseeable risks to health.

EPA Order 1000.17 goes beyond the Common Rule and bars risky and dangerous experiments on humans without good reason:

There is a presumption that studies involving risk of substantial injury to a human subject from the conduct of the study and that studies testing for irreversible health effects in humans will not be approved . . . unless strongly persuasive additional justification acceptable to the Review Official is submitted.

The Order goes on to state:

Any employee who has knowledge that EPA supported or conducted research has been associated with unexpected serious harm to one or more human subjects shall immediately notify the Review Official.

Once notified, the EPA Review Official then has the authority to suspend or terminate the study. With this legal framework, I presented to EPA Inspector General Elkins the EPA's conclusions and the claims it had made to the public and Congress about PM2.5.

The EPA's then-most recent scientific assessment of PM2.5, which had been published in December 2009, drew several conclusions.[60] The EPA had determined that the risk of death associated with PM2.5 increased by up to 1.21 percent for every 10 millionths-of-a-gram per cubic meter increase in PM2.5. This meant that the risk of death from PM2.5 was only zero when no PM2.5 was inhaled. Something that could never happen in the real world except possibly in some special chamber supplied with filtered air. Keep in mind that average U.S. outdoor air contains about 10 millionths-of-a-gram of PM2.5 per cubic meter.

The EPA also concluded in this document that the risk of death from PM2.5 was proportional to the level of PM2.5 inhalation—so the greater the exposure to PM2.5 the greater the risk of death. Perhaps most astonishingly, the EPA concluded that death from PM2.5 could occur within hours of inhaling, literally, a single particle. All these risks were then magnified, the EPA said, in "susceptible" populations like the elderly and the sick.

My letter to the EPA inspector general pointed out that these conclusions were more than mere fine print to be found deep in a

1,000-page long EPA document. They were broadcast by the EPA and presented as the basis for its proposed regulations. In July 2011, for example, the EPA's chairman of its Clean Air Scientific Advisory Committee, Jonathan Samet, wrote in the prestigious New England Journal of Medicine stating, "No thresholds have been identified below which there is no risk at all [from PM2.5].[61]

It was pointed out that EPA Administrator Jackson had testified to Congress about how PM2.5 didn't make you sick, it just killed you and that regulating it would be like "finding a cure for cancer"— that is, preventing 570,000 deaths per year.

Then there was the fact that EPA regulated PM2.5 on the basis that it killed people. In the *Federal Register* announcement of its final Cross-State Air Pollution rule, for example, the EPA stated,[62]

A recent EPA analysis estimated that 2005 levels of PM2.5 . . . [was] responsible for between 130,000 and 320,000 PM2.5-related premature deaths, or about 6.1 percent of total deaths from all causes in the continental U.S. (using the lower range for premature deaths). In other words, 1 in 20 deaths in the U.S. is attributable to PM2.5 . . .

In addition to the EPA-claimed lethality of PM2.5, the agency had also basically determined that PM2.5 caused cancer. In its 2009 scientific assessment of PM2.5, EPA stated:[63]

Evidence from epidemiologic and animal toxicologic studies has been accumulating for more than three decades regarding the mutagenicity and carcinogenicity of [particulate matter] in the ambient air . . .

Overall, the evidence is suggestive of a causal relationship between relevant PM2.5 exposures and cancer, with the strongest evidence coming from the epidemiologic studies of lung cancer mortality.

EPA had clearly determined that PM2.5 was ultra-hazardous stuff. The agency had concluded that individuals exposed to typical outdoor levels of PM2.5 could die within hours or days following exposure. Although typical outdoor air levels of PM2.5 were on the order of 10 micrograms per cubic meter, EPA had exposed its human subjects to levels of PM2.5 as high as 750 micrograms per cubic meter—that is, 75 times higher than what the EPA had already declared to be life-threatening.

So what part of this experiment didn't violate the letter and spirit of Common Rule or EPA Order 1000.17? The Order, for example, expressly barred "studies involving risk of substantial injury to a human subject from the conduct of a study" and "studies testing for irreversible health effects in humans," absent some strongly persuasive justification. Death certainly constituted a "substantial injury" and an "irreversible health effect," the letter stated.

In addition, the EPA claimed that PM2.5 caused cancer. How exactly were the EPA's PM2.5 experiments to square with what the U.S. Court of Appeals for the District of Columbia Circuit stated in its 1975 decision in *Environmental Defense Fund v. EPA*. In green-lighting the extrapolation of the results of pesticide testing on animals to humans, the Court observed:

> *The ethical problem of conducting cancer experiments on human beings are too obvious to require discussion.*

What was the point of all these human experiments anyway? The federal Common Rule required that risks to health and safety be reasonable in relation to the anticipated benefits of the experiment and not unnecessary. But the EPA had been regulating PM2.5 on the basis that it killed people since 1997. Having already determined and issued regulations on the basis of the lethality of PM2.5, why risk—if one believes the EPA's claims—the lives of the human study subjects?

The other key issue that needed to be addressed was that of informed consent. Had the EPA researchers adequately disclosed the risks of the PM2.5 experiments to the human study subjects so as to obtain the legally required informed consent? Was EPA as candid to the study subjects as it was, say, to Congress about the lethality of PM2.5? There was no evidence at this point that EPA hadn't obtained valid informed consent, but it was hard to believe that the agency had plainly told the study subjects that the experiments could result in their deaths as early as several hours afterwards.

My request for an investigation by the inspector general closed with citation of relevant precedent from federal appellate courts. In *Ethyl Corporation v. EPA*, a 1976 case involving the toxicity of leaded gasoline, the U.S. Court of Appeals for the District of Columbia Circuit wrote:[64]

> *Significant exposure to lead is toxic, so that considerations of decency and morality limit the flexibility of experiments on humans that would otherwise accelerate lead exposure from years to months and measures those results.*

But as "toxic" as the Court and EPA may have considered lead to be, that toxicity paled in comparison to the portrayal of PM2.5's near-instantaneous lethality.

In a 2001 case, a medical product liability case involving the medication Parlodel, the Eighth Circuit Court of Appeals noted:[65]

> *[Scientists] cannot perform controlled experiments because it would be unconscionable to induce strokes in postpartum women simply to advance the medical community's understanding of Parlodel.*

Substitute "death" for "strokes," "EPA" for "medical community" and "PM2.5" for "Parlodel" and EPA's PM2.5 experiments would be similarly "unconscionable," if not downright illegal.

I requested an investigation by the EPA inspector general into the PM2.5 experiments and sent copies to key Republican and

Democrat members of Congress who had responsibility for overseeing the EPA. But things would get a lot more interesting before anyone would respond.

CHAPTER 11

'Holy Cow!'

As mentioned earlier, the report of the cardiac arrhythmia experienced by the 58-year-old woman during the EPA experiment on her was published in a journal called Environmental Health Perspectives. The journal is published by a division of the National Institutes of Health (NIH) called the National Institute of Environmental Health Sciences (NIEHS). So in April of 2012 to follow up on the request for an investigation by the EPA's inspector general, I sent the editor of Environmental Health Perspectives, one Hugh Tilson, an email with the subject line "Request for Retraction:"

> *I am requesting that* Environmental Health Perspectives *take corrective action concerning the study 'Case Report: Supraventricular Arrhythmia after Exposure to Concentrated Ambient Air Pollution Particles,' ('Case Report') published online September 6, 2011.*
>
> *Based on information obtained through a Freedom of Information Act request made to the U.S. Environmental Protection Agency, the article omits material information about circumstances relevant to the Case Report. This omission materially affects the Case Report's discussion and conclusions.*

The case study, which is presented as evidence that fine particulate matter PM2.5 is a health risk, is not simply a lone "case study." The researchers in question, in fact, conducted 40 other experiments similar to the Case Report.

But Case Report contains no mention of these 40 other experiments—the results of which all contradict the conclusions drawn by the case study's authors.

'Case Report' should be retracted from publication and Environmental Health Perspectives *should commence an investigation of the authors' ethical conduct with respect to the Case Report.*

There is also an additional ethical concern with the Case Report—i.e., that the experiment involved exposing the study subject, who had a history of heart disease, to a potentially lethal level of PM2.5. It is the EPA's position, after all, that PM2.5 doesn't make one sick; it simply kills.

For more on the researcher's failure to protect a human subject and the nature of the 'lethality' of PM2.5, please read this article published in the Washington Times.

I am attaching for you the FOIA response from the EPA concerning the case study.

I look forward to your timely response.

A courtesy copy of the email was also sent to the members of the editorial board of the journal. Almost immediately after sending it, I received the following email from editorial board member Ken Korach, chief of the NIEHS Laboratory of Reproductive and Developmental Toxicology:

Holy cow—you didn't need this? What do you want us to do for you? Have you contacted the author about these claims?

Shortly thereafter, another email from Korach came in. This one read:

Steve:

Please disregard my previous message. The reply was to Hugh Tilson not to you. Sorry about the mis-sent message.

Ken

Korach's initial reaction went from shock ("Holy cow") to bureaucratic CYA—that is, "What do you want us to do for you?". Four days later, Tilson himself wrote back:

Dear Mr. Milloy,

> *I am acknowledging that we received your email.*
> *We have initiated steps to evaluate your allegation.*
> *I will inform you as soon as we have completed our inquiries.*

Sincerely,

Hugh A. Tilson, PhD
Editor-in-Chief
Environmental Health Perspectives

But it didn't take long for Tilson to complete his "inquiries." Three days later, I received by email a letter in which Tilson wrote in part:

Dear Mr. Milloy,

> *Thank you for your email of April 26, 2012 concerning the paper by Andrew Ghio et al. We have examined our records and I am reporting our findings in this letter.*
> *The observation reported in the Ghio et al paper was derived from a larger study conducted at the Human Studies Facility*

of the National Health and Environmental Research Laboratory of the U.S. Environmental Protection Agency. That study was an intentional environmental exposure study (ISEE), which involves controlled exposures made under rigorous experimental conditions. Informed consent was obtained from the participants prior to the onset of the study. The ISEE was approved by the University of North Carolina School of Medicine Committee on the Protection of the Rights of Human Subjects.

The purpose of the ISEE study was not to elicit supraventricular arrhythmias by exposure to concentrated ambient air pollutant particles. The observation in the Ghio et al *paper was an unintentional side effect in a single participant enrolled in the ISEE. Reporting the side effect was appropriate. Finally, the Ghio* et al *paper underwent rigorous peer-review before being accepted for publication.*

In summary, Ghio et al *observed a side effect during the course of a larger planned study and reported the side effect as a case report. The larger study had been approved by the university committee for the protection of the rights of human subjects and the participant described in the case report had provided informed consent prior to the onset of the study. Based on our findings, we see no reason for corrective action.*

Again, thank you for raising this issue. If you would like to raise other scientific or ethics questions about the Ghio et al *paper,* [Environmental Health Perspectives] *suggests that you write a letter to the editor. Note that Ghio et al will be given the opportunity to respond. As indicated in our instructions to Authors, a letter that is highly polemic or personal in nature will not be published. Correspondence is not peer reviewed and is published at the discretion of the* [Environmental Health Perspectives] *editors. Correspondence is limited to 750 words or less.*

Regards,

Hugh A. Tilson, PhD
Editor-in-Chief
Environmental Health Perspectives

The investigation into took no more than nine days. Based on the lack of substance in Tilson's response, it seemed no meaningful investigation of the allegations had occurred. Tilson's letter had not addressed the issues raised in the slightest.

On the substance, the Case Report as published in Environmental Health Perspectives made no mention whatsoever that the 58-year-old woman was only one of many subjects and that the totality of the results for these other human subjects entirely contradicted its conclusion (i.e., that its result "supports a causal relationship between" exposure to PM2.5 and heart disease). Environmental Health Perspectives had allowed EPA researchers to convert a freak, anecdotal incident—that could easily be explained by the 58-year-old woman's preexisting heart abnormality—into evidence that PM2.5 caused heart problems.

As to human experimentation, Tilson claimed the purpose of the experiment was not to cause heart problems. But of course, that's exactly what its purpose was. The experiment was conducted to see what happened to humans when exposed to very high levels of PM2.5. The researchers may not have expected to observe specifically a supraventricular arrhythmia, but that is no defense to the accusation that they experimented on people with a potentially lethal substance to see what would happen to them. Such experimentation would be per se unethical, if not illegal.

Finally, this was the second time the University of North Carolina had been cited as having reviewed and approved of the experiments. Possibly it did. But if so, did anyone tell the University of North Carolina that the EPA had concluded and, in fact, regulated on the basis that any inhalation of PM2.5 could cause death within hours?

Because Tiison dismissed the request for retraction, in May, I wrote to Don Wright, the director of the Office of Research Integrity for the Department of Health and Human Services, the parent agency of the NIEHS. One of the Office of Research Integrity's chief responsibilities is to investigate and make recommendations concerning misconduct by scientific researchers. So I asked Wright for an investigation into research misconduct on the part of Tilson.[66]

According to Department of Health and Human Services regulations, "researcher misconduct" includes:[67]

Omitting data or results such that the research is not accurately represented in the research record.

The plain language here certainly covers the omission of any mention of the other human study subjects in the EPA experiments; especially given the broad conclusion about PM2.5 drawn by the study authors.

The regulations regarding research misconduct also require that organizations within the Department of Health and Human Services, like the NIEHS, conduct bona fide investigations into misconduct allegations. So in managing an allegation, NIEHS was required to:[68]

Respond to each allegation of research misconduct for which the institution is responsible under this part in a thorough, competent, objective and fair manner, including precautions to ensure that individuals responsible for carrying out any part of the research misconduct proceeding do not have unresolved personal, professional, or financial conflicts of interest with the complainant, respondent or witnesses.

Conducting an investigation over the course of nine days was not "thorough, competent, objective or fair." I detailed each aspect of the claim pointing out how the Case Report was, in fact, research misconduct and how Tilson failed to conduct a thorough enough investigation.

A week later, the response came from the Office of Research and Integrity. Not surprisingly, it was not a favorable one. Wright stated that because his office's jurisdiction was limited to research funded by the Public Health Service and that the Case Report had been funded by the EPA, the matter was outside his jurisdiction. "For this reason, it was unnecessary for [Tilson] to take separate action regarding these allegations," the Office of Research Integrity letter stated.[69] So even though Tilson reviewed, edited and published the clearly defective paper in a journal funded by the Department of Health and Human Services, the Department's watchdog for research integrity would take no action.

I next tried Tilson's boss, Linda Birnbaum, director of NIEHS. Once again, the case was laid out that Tilson failed to adequately investigate the allegations about the Case Report. Once again, a mere week later, came her reply.

Birnbaum wrote in relevant part:

Thank you for your letter dated June 13, 2012. I appreciate your interest in environmental health research and your obvious dedication to scientific integrity. I share your commitment and therefore, conducted a thorough review of this matter.

In your letter, you contend that the editor of [Environmental Health Perspectives] *committed research misconduct by publishing this case report, because the manuscript described the results for only one study subject and did not mention the research findings for all other participants in the study. It is well understood among scientists and physicians that a case report is, in fact, an account of the results for a single person— and it represents an individual case. Publishing case reports is a very common practice and done frequently by the most respected biomedical journals including the* New England Journal of Medicine *and the* Journal of the American

Medical Association. *And although case reports represent research findings for a single study subject, they can be vitally important in helping medical doctors understand symptoms that may be seen in only a few people.*

In reviewing the manuscript, I saw that the authors . . . made it clear that the report represented results for one person . . .

I found that the authors included a thorough account of the subject's health status and family medical history, as well as the discovery of a pre-existing condition. I also found that the manuscript received rigorous scientific review prior to publication. In my opinion, the authors of this case report did not omit data or results. I believe that the manuscript accurately presented the research record for this case study and therefore, it was appropriate to publish the manuscript in Environmental Health Perspectives.

If you disagree with the authors' conclusions, I encourage you to write a Letter to the Editor for publication in Environmental Health Perspectives.

Once again, NIEHS dodged the issue. The problem with the Case Report was not that it was published at all—although it was odd that a medical case report was published in Environmental Health Perspectives as opposed to a standard medical journal read by physicians. Three of the study authors were, in fact, physicians. The problem was that the study was allowed to draw a general conclusion about PM2.5 causing heart problems without even hinting that there were at least dozens, if not hundreds, of other human study subjects in the same line of experiments each of whom represented conflicting data points, thereby drawing into question the claimed link with PM2.5.

As pointed out to Birnbaum in a follow-up letter:

Finally, as to your claim that the case report "received rigorous scientific review prior to publication," the reviewers (like readers) were axiomatically deceived by the manuscript's omission (falsification) of relevant data. It's too bad that we can't publicly poll the reviewers to see whether they are of the same "opinion" as you.

Not surprisingly, no response came from Birnbaum.

Before moving on from the NIEHS part of the human experiments saga, information about Tilson's actions after receiving the request for retraction are worth reviewing to get glimpse into the bureaucracy in CYA mode as revealed in emails obtained through the Freedom of Information Act.

On April 26, the day after Ken Korach accidentally sent me his "Holy Cow" response, Korach emailed Tilson:

Hugh:

I made a blunder—I replied to the message and thought it was going to you—I wrote back to Steve Milloy when I realized it and told him to disregard the message it was sent by mistake—I am very sorry—Ken

Tilson responded the next morning:

Hi Ken—no problem, good questions, though.
At present, I am letting the dust settle. I will contact EPA next week for additional information concerning the motivation for the study.

But according to a phone log received as part of the FOIA request, Tilson had already been in contact with Julian Preston, a senior official at the EPA laboratory where the human experiments had been conducted. There apparently were no records made of the subject of this call.

Korach emailed Tilson back the same morning, writing:

Hi Hugh:

I understand about some timing issues and not overreacting. You also need some clarifications from the authors and EPA without tipping your hand to EPA to the authors about what Milloy points out. See if you can get a candid reply from them. If they know someone has questioned the study then they'll put up a wall. Let me know if I can be of any help.

Ken

So Korach, at least, suspected the EPA researchers might be less than forthcoming about the experiments. Tilson immediately responded:

As I understand it, EPA spent the last week dealing with the issues raised by Milloy. So we were next in line.

Hugh

"Dealing with the issues raised by Milloy" resulted in the previously mentioned May 1 letter from EPA's Wayne Cascio published in the Washington Times.

Between April 27 and May 1, Tilson made phone calls about the request for retraction with several EPA officials, according to the phone log obtained. These EPA officials included Robert Kavlock, (Deputy Assistant Administrator for Science in EPA's Office of Research and Development), Wayne Cascio (Case Report co-author), Robert Devlin (senior scientist in EPA's human experiments program) Andrew Ghio (Case Report lead author) and Hal Zenick (Director of EPA's National Health and Environmental Effects Research Laboratory).

Then on May 3, 2012, Tilson emailed Christine Flowers (Director, NIEHS Office of Communications and Public Liaison) and Rick

Woychik (Deputy Director of NIEHS) about his draft response to my letter:

I would appreciate your feedback on the letters. I have not discussed this issue with anyone else at this point.

The letter was apparently approved without further discussion—even though the FOIA-ed documents show Tilson contacted senior EPA staffers related to the controversy, yet does not mention that in the e-mail.

It was weird, but then, what hadn't been so far?

The take home message from these interactions with the NIEHS staff reinforced the conviction that PM2.5 hurt no one. If PM2.5 actually did kill or harm people, no one at the NIEHS would likely have been so nonchalant about the allegations. Additionally, no one at NIEHS appeared to be upset about the EPA saying one thing about PM2.5 and then acting in an entirely inconsistent and unethical manner. The NIEHS either didn't care about the EPA's apparent ethical lapses or preferred to ignore them. Whatever the explanation, the NIEHS's conduct reflected poorly on the agency and government science.

CHAPTER 12

No Time for Bioethics

While these exchanges with NIEHS were ongoing, I wrote to the chairman of the Presidential Commission for the Study of Bioethical Issues, Dr. Amy Gutmann:

> *The U.S. Environmental Protection Agency has conducted unethical, if not illegal, human experiments.*
>
> *I am requesting that the Presidential Commission for the study of Bioethical Issues conduct an independent investigation of the experiments in question and report its findings to the public.*
>
> *Enclosed please find a copy of the request for investigation that I recently sent to the U.S. Environmental Protection Agency's Office of Inspector General, which details the allegations.*

The Presidential Executive Order that created the Commission stated in the "Mission" section that:

> *The Commission may examine . . . the protection of human research participants.*

In addition, Guttman, the president of the University of Pennsylvania and was keenly aware of Nazi barbarity as revealed in a June 2011 interview with the *New York Times*:[70]

73

Question. *What do you consider some of your most important leadership lessons?*

Answer. *The biggest influences on me for leading preceded my ever even thinking of myself as a leader—particularly my father's experience leaving Nazi Germany. Because I would not even exist if it weren't for his combination of courage and farsightedness. He saw what was coming with Hitler and he took all of his family and left for India. That took a lot of courage. That is always something in the back of my mind.*

Several months after this interview, Gutmann's Commission had issued a report condemning U.S. Public Health Service experiments on poor Guatemalans during the 1940s. In what can only be described as the Tuskegee syphilis experiments on steroids, the researchers "deliberately exposed about 1,300 inmates, psychiatric patients, soldiers and commercial sex workers to sexually transmitted diseases syphilis, gonorrhea, or chancroid," all of which happened without any informed consent.[71] It is unethical, of course, for researchers to intentionally infect anyone with sexually transmitted diseases, even if they can obtain consent.

So I thought Gutmann might be a sympathetic ear. After all, the allegation was that government researchers at the EPA were intentionally exposing people to PM2.5, which EPA had determined could be immediately lethal after any inhalation of it. It was also alleged that informed consent probably had not been obtained from the human study subjects.

Though the letter was hand-delivered to Gutmann's office at the University of Pennsylvania, two weeks later on May 31, 2012, the response came from one Michelle Groman, associate director of the Commission. The letter read:

Dear Mr. Milloy,

I am writing on behalf of Dr. Amy Gutmann and the Presidential Commission for the Study of Bioethical Issues to thank you for your letter.

As you may know, the Commission has completed its assessment of current human research standards. On December 15, 2011, it issued its report concerning federally sponsored research involving human volunteers, concluding that current regulations generally appear to protect people from avoidable harm or unethical treatment.

The Commission currently has a full agenda for the upcoming year. The commission is working on projects that concern, first access to and privacy of human genome sequence data; second, the development of medical [bioterror] countermeasures for children; and third, neuroscience and related ethical issues.

We will retain your letter and consider your comments in connection with future activities as applicable. The Commission appreciates your taking time to write us and your interest in our work.

With best wishes,

Michelle Groman, J.D.
Associate Director

Another non-response.

A 2011 report from Gutmann's Commission confirmed what I had been uncovering about government-sponsored human experiments. According to the Commission:[72]

The current U.S. system provides substantial protections for the health, rights and welfare of research subjects and, in

*general, serves to 'protect people from harm or unethical treat-
ment' when they volunteer to participate as subjects in scientific
studies supported by the federal government. However, because
of the currently limited ability of some governmental agencies
to identify basic information about all of their human subjects
research, <u>the Commission cannot say that all federally funded
research provides optimal protections against avoidable harms
and unethical treatment</u>. The Commission finds significant
room for improvement in several areas where, for example,
immediate changes can be made to increase accountability
and thereby reduce the likelihood of harm or unethical treatment.* [Emphasis added]

One reason the Presidential Commission couldn't guarantee
federal agencies optimally protect their human subjects is, as explained
in the media release for the report:[73]

*The Commission requested information from 18 individual
agencies that conduct most federal human subjects research,
but discovered that many federal offices could not provide basic
data about the research they support.*

While the EPA was one of the agencies that provided the Commission
with "basic data," those data appear to have been little more than
accounting-type data. That is, a tally of how many human subjects
studies the agency had conducted, whether they were conducted in
the U.S. or abroad and how much money in grants the EPA gave to
non-agency scientists to conduct human experiments. There was no
review of what human experiments were being conducted, why they
were being conducted, or any other in-depth examination or audit of
what the EPA was doing with its human studies subjects.

Because of the Commission's superficial review of federally sponsored human experiments, it missed a glaring difference between
EPA's human experiments and human experiments conducted by

say the National Institutes of Health (NIH). The Commission viewed human experiments as:[74]

> *The paradigmatic example of this sort of research circumstance is the typical Phase I trial of a new but traditional cytotoxic oncologic agent that holds promise in animal studies but has not yet been tried in human beings. The purpose of such a study is to determine toxicity and tolerability in human beings. The subjects enrolling in such trials are typically patients with advanced malignancies for which all standard therapeutic options have failed.*

To the Commission, then, human experiments were typically medical or therapeutic in nature—desperately sick people willing to undertake experimental risks in hopes of a treatment or cure that will benefit them personally. But this is not at all what the EPA was doing with its human subjects.

As EPA official and human experimenter Wayne Cascio disclosed in his letter to the Washington Times, the EPA was perversely experimenting on healthy people for the purpose of validating the agency's epidemiologic claims about PM2.5 killing people.

I wrote back to Gutmann in June requesting reconsideration of the request for review:[75]

> *My letter provided you with prima facie evidence that a federal agency recently violated every core ethical principle and federal regulation concerning human experimentation, thereby flagrantly risking the lives of at least 41 humans.*
>
> *Your response was, essentially, that the Commission is too busy to consider my allegations. It's perhaps no wonder that the Commission concluded in its December 15, 2011 report that current regulations 'appear to protect people from avoidable harm [and] unethical treatment.' The regulations only 'appear' protective because there's been no actual investigation.*

One week later, another response from another Commission bureaucrat arrived. After summarizing the Commission's mission statement, executive director Lisa M. Lee wrote:

> *The Commission is not a law enforcement, regulatory, or legislative body and per its establishing Executive Order . . . it 'shall not be responsible for the review and approval of specific projects.' Although the Commission may accept suggestions of issue for consideration from the public, the Commission must consider, among other things, 'the availability of other appropriate entities or fora for deliberating on the issues' in prioritizing its activities.*
>
> *Given that, first, the Commission does not have authority to review specific cases, second, the Commission is currently working on three projects . . . and, third, it appears that other appropriate entities are available to consider your claims, the Commission cannot undertake the independent review that you request.*

So let's conduct a thought experiment. Let's pretend it's 1972 and Gutmann is the chief of an official government body chartered to oversee the protection of human subjects in scientific research. A whistleblower writes Gutmann describing that hundreds of poor, uneducated black men in Alabama are not having their syphilis treated so that rogue U.S. government researchers can observe the natural course of the disease. Would Gutmann instruct her staff to respond to the whistleblower by saying that her organization wasn't responsible for specific projects and was too busy to pay attention? Perhaps that's the sort of bureaucratic no-man's land that forced the Tuskegee syphilis experiments whistleblower to take his story to the media in order to get action.

CHAPTER 13

What Hippocratic Oath?

By the summer of 2012, the EPA's human experiments with PM2.5 were about to get a lot more interesting. But before they did, more letters were fired off in an effort to find someone in a position of authority who would be concerned, if not actually appalled, by the EPA's experiments.

I appealed to the North Carolina Medical Board, the state organization responsible for investigating and disciplining the conduct of physicians. Three of the co-authors of the Case Report were physicians licensed in the state of North Carolina.

That letter cited a version of the modern Hippocratic oath used at the University of North Carolina School of Medicine:[76]

> *I do solemnly swear by all I hold most sacred . . . that I will exercise my art for the benefit of my patients, the relief of the suffering, the prevention of disease and promotion of health and I will give no drug and perform no act for an immoral purpose.*

The Medical Board appeared to take this oath very seriously as it had previously barred physicians from participating in the execution of judicially sanctioned death sentences. While the EPA's human guinea pigs had not been condemned to death by any court of law,

the EPA certainly seemed bent on proving its claims about the lethality of PM2.5 at their expense, even if it cost them their lives.

I pointed out that Case Report physicians Drs. Andrew Ghio,
Eugene Chung and Wayne Cascio had violated the Common Rule
and EPA Order 1000.17 in conducting the experiments. "Given
that these rules exist solely to protect the safety of human subjects
from dangerous experimentation, their violation is anything but
virtuous or honorable" as contemplated by the Hippocratic Oath.

It was also noted that Drs. Ghio, Chung and Cascio had intentionally exposed 41 human subjects to the allegedly ultra-hazardous
PM22.5 for the sole purpose of causing health problems and that
according to their own report, "at least one patient was in fact harmed
by the experiment." As the human subjects stood to gain nothing
from the experiment, this conduct violated the Hippocratic Oath's
command to act "solely for the benefit" of patients.

Since North Carolina law empowered the Medical Board to
discipline physicians for immoral, dishonorable, or unprofessional
conduct, I asked it to undertake a thorough investigation, release
the findings to the public and to take any disciplinary action that
may be warranted. A few days after filing the complaint, the Medical
Board responded, stating that, "Every complaint filed with the Board
is taken seriously and carefully reviewed and that each review may
take six months or more.[77]

As the University of North Carolina School of Medicine acted
as the EPA's Institutional Review Board for the PM2.5 experiments,
I also sent a letter to the University of North Carolina Medical
School. Addressing the dean of the school, Dr. William Roper, it read:[78]

Dear Dean Roper,

*I am writing to alert you to illegal human testing involving
the University of North Carolina School of Medicine
(UNC) and its staff.*

The illegal acts are described in available detail in the [attached letter I sent to the EPA's inspector general]. They involve the UNC's Office of Human Research Ethics and an employee of the Division of Cardiology.

The conduct in question may expose UNC to significant civil liability and reputational harm.

I request that you conduct a bona fide investigation of these allegations and report your findings to the public promptly.

Sincerely,

Steve Milloy

A little more than two weeks later, I received a response from Dean Roper that read:[79]

Dear Mr. Milloy,

Thank you for your letter of June 12, 2012. We take the conduct and oversight of research seriously at UNC-Chapel Hill and expect our investigators and review boards to follow all applicable policies and regulations, including the Common Rule for protection of human subjects. We are reviewing the circumstances of the studies cited in your letter and will investigate further if warranted.

Sincerely,

William L. Roper

But by the time Dean Roper responded, I had received all the information I needed to know what the EPA was—and was not—disclosing to all involved.

CHAPTER 14

Damning Documents

About the same time as the correspondence with UNC-Chapel Hill, I received a call from staff assistants at the House Committee on Space, Science and Technology. Following up on the *Washington Times* commentary comparing the EPA experiments to the Tuskegee syphilis experiments, committee staff had requested a briefing from the EPA about the human experiments. The actual briefing turned out be a hard-to-hear conference call during which time the EPA tried to tamp down the allegations.

The EPA staff had also provided to the committee all remaining documents related to the outstanding FOIA request—documents I wouldn't receive directly from the EPA for another six weeks. But the committee staff sent me the documents as soon as it received them. The 496 pages answered a lot of questions—none in the EPA's favor.

I had requested:

1. *The protocols and consent forms that were approved by the University of North Carolina School of Medicine Committee on the protection of Human Subjects;*

2. *The informed consent forms for the 41 study subjects involved in the [human experiments disclosed via my*

*initial Freedom of Information Act request made in
the September 2011]; and*

3. *Any and all related documents submitted to and approved by the U.S. EPA Program in Research Ethics.*

The documents, mostly forms used to obtain informed consent
from the study subjects, revealed that the 41 human study subjects
had participated in three EPA-conducted experiments with the
somewhat ironic names, KINGCON, XCON and OMEGACON.

In the KINGCON study, EPA had experimented on human
study subjects between the ages of 45 to 65 years of age who had
mild asthma and a specific gene to see if they were "especially susceptible to air pollution."[80] Not that any potential human study
subject would have any reason to know this, but the EPA had already
determined much earlier that older people were more "susceptible"
than young people to "air pollution." In its 1996 scientific assessment
for PM2.5, which served as the basis of its 1997 regulations, the EPA
determined that:[81]

> *There is considerable agreement among different studies that
> the elderly are particularly susceptible to effects from both
> short-term and long-term exposures to PM, especially if they
> have underlying respiratory or cardiac disease.*

As EPA had already long been regulating PM2.5 on the basis that
older people were more susceptible to its effects, these tests were
axiomatically unnecessary—and unnecessary human experiments
ran afoul of the Common Rule's prohibition against exposing human
subjects to "unnecessary" risk, that is if there was any actual risk
posed by PM2.5.[82]

The KINGCON consent form described the exposure to the
PM2.5 to participants as follows:[83]

During the exposure you will: undergo a chamber exposures [sic] of 2 hours duration, once to clean air and at the other sessions to concentrated Chapel Hill particles; the amount of particles you will be exposed to is less than what you would likely encounter over 24 hours on a smoggy day in an urban area . . .

The exposure chamber is 4 feet wide by 6.25 feet in height and is 8 feet in length . . .. During the two-hour exposures you will be asked to breathe air through a facemask that is secured by a headband.

But the question remained: Had EPA told the study subjects that the agency's scientists had concluded that PM2.5 could kill and that death could come mere hours after inhalation of any level of PM2.5? The form stated in relevant part:

What are the possible risks or discomforts involved with being in this study?

During the exposure to the concentrated air pollution particles, you may experience some minor degree of airway irritation, cough and shortness of breath or wheezing. Some studies suggest that persons with asthma may be at risk for developing an asthma attack as a result of exposure to fine air pollution particles. These symptoms typically disappear 2 to 4 hours after exposure, but may last longer for particularly sensitive people . . .

Air pollution particles may induce an inflammatory reaction that can last for 24 hours after exposure and may increase your chance of catching a cold. You should not engage in heavy levels of exercise for 24 hours before and after the exposure period. There is a small possibility that you could have more asthma symptoms for several days and even less likely, for several weeks after the particle exposure. This flare in your asthma would be similar to what happens to you and other asthmatics during the allergy season or with a viral infection. Such a flare is considered highly unlikely and the exposure risk is comparable to walking around a major metropolitan area such as Los Angeles or Houston during a smoggy day.

So was Lisa Jackson's statement to Congress false? "Particulate matter causes premature death. It doesn't make you sick. It's directly causal to dying sooner than you should?" What happened to the Common Rule regulatory requirement of obtaining *informed* consent? The Common Rule specifically requires that:[84]

No investigator may involve a human being as a subject in research covered by this policy unless the investigator has obtained the legally effective informed consent of the subject or the subject's legally authorized representative.

A "basic element of informed consent," according to the Common Rule, includes:[85]

A description of any reasonably foreseeable risks or discomforts to the subject.

Is death from PM2.5 "reasonably foreseeable?" Furthermore, EPA chief Lisa Jackson told Congress that PM2.5 was responsible for more than 1-in-5 deaths in the U.S. every year. The EPA's scientific assessments of PM2.5 determined that any inhalation could result in death in hours or days. The EPA officials repeatedly told Congress and the public that there was no safe exposure to PM2.5. None of this was disclosed to KINGCON human study subjects.

Because there was no disclosure of the risk of death from inhaling PM2.5, the study subjects could not have provided informed consent to the experiments—even if consent for such experimentation were permissible in the first place. Without informed consent, the EPA experiments violated federal regulations and state law, and were, therefore, illegal.

So the EPA didn't disclose the risk of death from inhaling PM2.5 to the study subjects. Did the agency at least mention it to the University of North Carolina Institutional Review Board responsible for approving the experiments? No. There was no mention of death or of any potentially serious adverse health effect. The EPA told the University of North Carolina Institutional Review Board that it wanted to conduct the experiment, it stated, merely to learn how inhaling PM2.5 might "affect" the cardiovascular system. The EPA's failure to mention the possibility of death was not limited to just the KINGCON experiment.

The next study, XCON, showed similar discrepancies. In this study, adults between the ages of 25 years and 70 years with metabolic syndrome were exposed to ultrafine particulate matter at levels up to 60 times greater than in outdoor air. People with metabolic syndrome are at increased risk of heart disease and diabetes as indicated by their abdominal obesity, blood chemistry and higher than normal blood pressure. Ultrafine particles are discrete particles like PM2.5, but they are much smaller than PM2.5—about one millionth of a meter in diameter as compared to PM2.5's 2.5 millionths of a meter.

While the EPA had not and still does not yet regulate ultrafine particles in outdoor air, the agency has been studying whether regulation is needed since at least the year 2000. Toward that end, the EPA commissioned a five-year study of outdoor levels of ultrafine particles and daily deaths in Erfurt, Germany.[86] According to the March 2005 report of the study, ultrafine particulate matter in outdoor air was thought to kill people in essentially the same hours-to-days time frame as PM2.5 But this conclusion was not disclosed to the Institutional Review Board. The EPA told the University of North Carolina Institutional Review Board that:

Particle exposure is not expected to produce any permanent adverse health effects at the concentrations being used in this study.

Despite that statement in the Institutional Review Board application, the EPA provided study subjects with the following disclosure in the consent form:[87]

During one of the exposure sessions you will be exposed to air containing mostly contaminated ultra-fine air pollution particles (this air may contain some larger particles as well). The risks associated with concentrated particle exposure in people with metabolic syndrome are unknown. Some studies suggest that elderly people, particularly those with underlying cardiovascular disease are at increased risk for getting sick and even dying during episodes of high air pollution. At this time, no one understands exactly how these particles might cause people to become sick or die . . . we cannot exclude the possibility that you may have an adverse reaction to breathing these particles

So the EPA mentioned in XCON that "some studies suggest" that people may die from PM2.5, especially the elderly and the sick. The agency did not, however for the benefit of study subjects, clearly connect that research with the XCON experiment. The EPA omitted to inform the study subjects that the agency had already determined—as opposed to "some studies suggest"—that PM2.5 caused death in the short-term and that they were about to get a mega-dose of it.

In the OMEGACON experiments, the EPA not only intentionally exposed study subjects to PM2.5 to see what would happen to them, but the researchers had the study subjects consume either a fish oil supplement or a placebo (olive oil) for 30 days before the PM2.5 exposure experiment. The purpose of the experiment was to see whether omega-3 fatty acid supplementation (from the fish oil) would reduce the presumptive "adverse cardiovascular effects" of the

PM2.5 exposure. Once again, the University of North Carolina Institutional Review Board was left in the dark about what the EPA had already officially determined to be the risks of breathing PM2.5.

What information was disclosed to study subjects in the consent form? It stated:[88]

> *During the exposure to concentrated air pollution particles, you may experience some minor degree of airway irritation, cough and shortness of breath or wheezing. These symptoms typically disappear 2 to 4 hours after exposure, but may last longer for particularly sensitive people . . .*
>
> *Air pollution particles may induce an inflammatory reaction that can last for 24 hours after exposure and may increase the chance of you catching a cold . . .*

But catching a cold isn't nearly the same as dying.

CHAPTER 15

Suing the EPA

The EPA had concluded in its scientific assessments, scared the public into believing and repeatedly told Congress that inhaling PM2.5 was deadly—and not simply deadly over a lifetime of breathing it but within hours or days of breathing it. PM2.5 was effectively the most lethal substance known to man. Yet none of the human study subjects participating in the agency's KINGCON, XCON or OMEGACON studies had been informed of that fact.

I had raised the issue in the media. I had raised the issue with the EPA and its inspector general. I had raised the issue with the government-run journal that had published the Case Report and with the journal's agency, the NIEHS. I had raised the issue with the Department of Health and Human Services' Office of Research Integrity as well as the Presidential Commission for the Study of Bioethics. I had raised the issued with the University of North Carolina School of Medicine, where the experiments had occurred. I had raised the issue with the North Carolina Medical Board and, finally, with Congress.

Yet as of September 2012, four months after the Washington Times op-ed, "Did Obama's EPA Relaunch the Tuskegee Experiments," no one outside a few congressional staffers were willing to take an interest in the EPA's human experiments. So I sued the EPA—using its own words and claims about PM2.5 against it.

There were two main issues regarding the EPA's claims about the lethality of PM2.5. First, the EPA human experiments with PM2.5 were fundamentally unethical and impermissible, if not illegal under the Common Rule. Since PM2.5 was essentially a deadly substance, the experiments were fundamentally unethical because human study subjects were asked to accept the risk of death in a non-therapeutic experiment.

Unlike traditional medical research, the subjects' lives were put at risk not in order to treat or save them from some serious disease or condition from which they suffered, but instead for the sole and improper purpose of advancing the EPA's regulatory programs. As the EPA informed the OMEGACON study subjects:[89]

> *You will not directly benefit from being in this research . . . This research is designed to benefit society by gaining new knowledge. Given that every member of American society is currently exposed to these pollutants, this study has the potential to contribute toward devising effective strategies aimed at protecting millions from the untoward effects of these pollutants.*

If it's not commonsense that a government agency may not risk the lives of study subjects merely for the sake of its regulatory program, the Common Rule expressly bars that reason as grounds for risking human subjects in scientific experiments.

The rule states risks to subjects must be:[90]

> *. . . reasonable in relation to anticipated benefits, if any, to subjects and the importance of the knowledge that may reasonably be expected to result. In evaluating risks and benefits, the Institutional Review Board (IRB) should consider only those risks and benefits that may result from the research (as distinguished from risks and benefits of therapies subjects would receive even if not participating in the research). The IRB should not consider possible long-range effects of applying*

knowledge gained in the research (for example, the possible effects of the research on public policy) as among those research risks that fall within the purview of its responsibility.
[Emphasis added]

The second reason was that the EPA failed to obtain the legally required informed consent. Though the EPA told the public and Congress that any inhalation of PM2.5 was potentially lethal within hours of inhalation and the EPA also regulated outdoor air quality on that basis, agency researchers failed to disclose any of this information to the study subjects in the consent forms they were to sign. But as the Common Rule states,[91]

Except as provided elsewhere in this policy, no investigator may involve a human being as a subject in research covered by this policy unless the investigator has obtained the legally effective informed consent . . .

The "basic elements of informed consent" include:

A description of any reasonably foreseeable risks or discomforts to the subject . . .

Of the exceptions to obtaining informed consent, the only one in the Common Rule that could possibly be applied was:

The research involves no more than minimal risk to the subjects . . .

The key term in that exception is "minimal risk." What does that mean? The Common Rules states:

Minimal risk means that the probability and magnitude of harm or discomfort anticipated in the research are not greater in and of themselves than those ordinarily encountered in daily life or during the performance of routine physical or psychological examinations or tests.

So while the EPA claimed that any exposure to PM2.5 could cause death within hours of inhalation and all outdoor air contained some PM2.5—about 10 millionths-of-a-gram per cubic meter of air—nowhere in America can one find outdoor air containing the extreme levels of PM2.5 the EPA made the human subjects inhale. Those levels could exceed 600 or more millionths-of-a-gram per cubic meter of air, which is more than 17 times higher than the EPA's acute exposure standard for outdoor air and 60 times higher than typical U.S. outdoor air. And since nearly instantaneous death was a possibility and since PM2.5 killed 570,000 people in the U.S. per year, the EPA did not meet the "minimal risk" threshold.

Suing the government is challenging to say the least. The basic problem is one of sovereign immunity. You can't sue the government unless it specifically allows you. Although the EPA had clearly violated the Common Rule, for example, the regulation provides no mechanism for the public—or really for anyone else—to enforce its provisions.

The Common Rule does contain a section entitled, "Administrative Actions for Noncompliance," but those regulations merely would have allowed the EPA to take action against the University of North Carolina School of Medicine by disqualifying its Institutional Review Board or debarring researchers from future the EPA funding. But none of that was going to happen. The University of North Carolina Institutional Review Board was doing to the bidding of EPA management in green-lighting the experiments. The researchers weren't the recipients of EPA grants, but were instead EPA employees.

So suing the EPA over the Common Rule itself, then, would not get very far in court.

My lawyer on the case was David Schnare of the Free Market Environmental Law Clinic. He suggested that we go into federal court and ask a court to stop an ongoing or planned human experiment at the EPA. He said we could sue the EPA under the declaratory judgment provisions of section 2201 of the U.S. Code, which allows a plaintiff to go to "any court of the United States, upon the filing of an appropriate pleading" so that the court "may declare the rights and other legal relations of any interested party seeking such declaration . . ." We could ask a court for a declaratory judgment that the EPA was violating the Common Rule and that as part of the complaint we also ask for the court to issue an injunction barring the EPA from conducting illegal human experiments.

All that was required was an appropriate and ongoing human experiment being conducted by the EPA. This was easy enough to find. The EPA employed a contractor that maintained a website for recruiting its human guinea pigs. We found the ongoing CAPTAIN experiment in which the EPA was planning to expose subjects between the ages of 50 to 75 years to PM2.5 for the purpose of seeing whether the experiments caused changes to the heart.

So far so good, but Schnare said we would still have to show the court that we had standing—that is, the right to bring the action in federal court in the first place.

Schnare's idea was to mimic what environmental activist groups often do, that is, sue on behalf of their "aggrieved" members and hope the court takes the case. We couldn't use past or present EPA human study subjects as "aggrieved" members for the simple reason that we didn't know who they were and the EPA would not tell us.

So we enlisted a non-profit group to which Schnare belonged, the American Tradition Institute, an "organization dedicated to the advancement of rational, free-market solutions to America's land, energy and environmental challenges [with] members throughout the nation."

The American Tradition Institute's aggrieved members would be a fellow named Landon Huffman, Schnare and myself. Huffman had actually been one of EPA's guinea pigs in experiments who had contacted me via email after reading some of the early media accounts of EPA's human experiments.

Huffman's grievance was stated as follows:

In November 2006 and May 2007 Mr. Huffman participated in human experimentation conducted by the U.S. Environmental Protection Agency (EPA) of the kind at issue in this matter.

He received a consent form that did not explain that he would be exposed to something that the EPA claims to be lethal. Nor was he ever informed that human experimentation was only supposed to be done in a manner that would potentially and directly benefit those subjected to human experimentation.

He was lead to believe that the benefit of the experiment would be to help people with asthma, something from which he suffers. He was not informed that the pollution EPA was forcing into his lungs could actually cause him to have an asthma attack. Nor was he ever given anything from EPA that would possibly relieve his asthma.

Since learning that the EPA considers the gases to which he was exposed were lethal, he has been distraught and experienced emotional distress, such as a fear of becoming ill or dying. His health is of utmost importance to him and he is disturbed by the fact that because of his participation in EPA's human experimentation, his health is in greater jeopardy than when he voluntarily agreed to participate in those studies. As a result of those studies, he is distressed that he may not be able to provide for his wife and family in the short-term as well as long-term.

He is also distressed that others may suffer the way he does if they participate in ongoing studies. He believes no one should be falsely and unknowingly exposed to a lethal gas and only by stopping this human experimentation will he be relieved of his continuing concern that others not suffer what he now does.

Huffman couldn't sue the EPA on his own because the statute of limitations had run out on what would have been his claim. Schnare was aggrieved because:[92]

> Dr. Schnare's parents selected his name, David, to honor the last male relative to die before his birth. That man's name was David Steiner, a Jew who died in Buchenwald concentration camp on May 3, 1945, 21 days after the camp was liberated. Tattooed on his body was the number 59059.
>
> German physicians conducted large-scale human experimentation at Buchenwald. Some 729 inmates were used as test subjects, of whom 154 died. This human experimentation included determining the dose of a poison necessary to cause death.
>
> Dr. Schnare more than abhors current governmental experimentation on humans for the purposes of determining the effect of poisons. It is not only that such activity dishonors those who should have been the last to have suffered in such a manner, it sickens and angers him. It causes him to stand up for those who could not and cannot. Dr. Schnare does not hold the name David as a whim or merely as a naming tradition. He views his name as an honor to one who did not survive the horrors of a government utterly without ethics. He believes he can do no less than rise in opposition to any government who would experiment on subjects without their well-informed willingness and where they have they do not have the opportunity to personally benefit from such an experiment.
>
> Dr. Schnare was employed by the U.S. Environmental Protection Agency for 33 years, first as a scientist and policy analyst, finally as an enforcement attorney. In the last years with the Agency, he realized that EPA had abandoned much of the even-handed, science-based approach to protection of human health and the environment which marked its early

years and left the Agency, in part, because senior appointees and employees had rejected the core values held by honest scientists and civil servants. When he learned of the human experimentation at issue in this case, he realized a duty to challenge EPA's misanthropic activities, if for no other reason than to preserve his own legacy of having worked assiduously on behalf of public health.

The University of North Carolina (UNC) awarded Dr. Schnare a Doctor of Philosophy in Environmental Management and its School of Public Health awarded him a Master of Science in Public Health. During his graduate matriculation at UNC, he served on the Dean's Cabinet, the advisory and decision-making body assisting the Dean of the School of Public Health. Among the many subjects addressed during his tenure on the Cabinet, the Dean and Faculty took special interest in ensuring the faculty fully complied with all requirements mandated by the Institutional Review Board (IRB) and federal and state statutes and rules dealing with human experimentation.

After learning of how EPA failed to honestly represent the nature of the human experimentation that is the subject of the instant matter, he was appalled that the UNC Biomedical IRB review process failed to conduct the kind of independent review necessary to ensure the representations by EPA were not only true but complete and fully reflected EPA's knowledge about the poisons with which they intended to force into the lungs of unsuspecting and inadequately informed human subjects. As an alumnus of the University, he is deeply upset at this failure and it adds to his great angst and the emotional harm he suffers from the on-going illegal human experimentation.

The relief sought in the instant matter will significantly ameliorate his suffering and will help return honor to the memory of David Steiner and all those who died at the hands of the "Doctors from Hell."

Finally, my particular grievance was stated as follows:

One of the great horrors Mr. Milloy and his family suffer is the memory of the incarceration of Mr. Milloy's uncle, Zoran Galkanovic, at the Mauthausen concentration camp. Upon threat of death, Mr. Galkanovic was forced to rise each morning and identify those individuals at the concentration camp too ill to work, knowing they would subsequently be executed . . .

German physicians conducted large-scale human experimentation at the Mauthausen concentration camp. 'German doctors subjected Mauthausen prisoners to pseudoscientific medical experiments, including testing levels of testosterone, experimenting with delousing chemicals, medicines for tuberculosis and nutrition experiments. Camp physician Hermann Richter surgically removed significant organs—e.g., stomach, liver, or kidneys—from living prisoners solely in order to determine how long a prisoner could survive without the organ in question. Eduard Krebsbach, the executive camp doctor between autumn 1941 and autumn 1943, killed an undetermined number of prisoners by injecting phenol directly into their hearts.'

'It was behind the gray stone walls of Mauthausen, in his native Austria, that Dr. [Aribert] Heim committed the atrocities against hundreds of Jews and others that earned him the nickname Dr. Death and his status as the most wanted Nazi war criminal still believed by the Simon Wiesenthal Center to be at large. Dr. Heim was accused of performing operations on prisoners without anesthesia; removing organs from healthy inmates, then leaving them to die on the operating table; injecting poison, including gasoline, into the hearts of others; and taking the skull of at least one victim as a souvenir.

Because of the inhumanity forced on Mr. Galkanovic, Mr. Milloy has accepted as a family responsibility for the fight against any government who subjects its citizens to inhumane treatment. He is deeply aggrieved by the kind of human experimentation being conducted by the U.S. EPA and will not be relieved until it stops.

After learning of how the U.S. Environmental Protection Agency was risking the lives and health of human study subjects and was failing to honestly represent the nature of the human experimentation that is the subject of the instant matter, Mr. Milloy was appalled by this inhumanity.

Mr. Milloy has dedicated a majority of his current work effort to expose and stop the EPA's improper, unethical and illegal human experimentation. Mr. Milloy is deeply aggrieved by the kind of human experimentation being conducted by the U.S. Environmental Protection Agency and will not be relieved until it stops.

Mr. Milloy owns and maintains two websites dedicated to exposing government excess and dishonest science. Since 1996, JunkScience.com has been dedicated to exposing the abuse of science by special interests, including the EPA. Since September 2012, EPAHumanTesting.com has focused on exposing EPA's unlawful and immoral failure to protect human study subjects. These efforts reflect Mr. Milloy's dedication to ensuring honest, ethical government, especially in cases where the government engages in science and human experimentation.

We were hopeful that a federal judge would find these arguments at least as compelling as some environmentalist upset about the thought that some part of the world was not a pristine as it could be.

The complaint stated the facts and law against EPA as in the following paragraph headers:

The EPA says PM2.5 can be lethal within hours of exposure.

The EPA believes there is no safe level of PM2.5.

The EPA has exposed human subjects to lethal levels of PM2.5.

The EPA intends to gas additional humans with PM2.5.

The law only allows for limited experimentation on humans.

The EPA did not properly inform its human subjects.

The EPA did not properly inform the Institutional Review Board.

The Institutional Review Board failed in its duties.

The EPA's PM2.5 research conduct is a shocking violation of acceptable moral and ethical norms.

The complaint closed by asking the court to issue an order halting the EPA's CAPTAIN study and any similar study until a competent IRB could approve an application for human experimentation that met all relevant standards.

We filed the complaint on September 25, 2012. Shortly thereafter, we filed for a temporary restraining order against EPA conducting any more human experiments.

CHAPTER 16

Selective Outrage

While the EPA had about two weeks to respond to the court regarding our motion for a temporary restraining order, the agency responded to a media inquiry right away. The EPA told the *Washington Times:*[93]

> *The EPA is one of 15 federal departments and agencies that conduct or support research with human subjects under the governance of the Common Rule. All human exposure studies conducted by the EPA scientists are independently evaluated for safety and ethics and the results are peer-reviewed. The complaint has been referred to the Department of Justice and further inquiry regarding litigation should be directed to them.*

As pointed out on JunkScience.com at the time, the merits of the EPA's response depended on the meaning of "independently evaluated." Recall that the University of North Carolina acted as the EPA's Institutional Review Board on a contract basis. Besides that, the EPA records showed that the University of North Carolina had received more than $33 million in grants from the EPA.[94] In addition, the EPA's testing facility was located on the grounds of the university's medical school campus. So the EPA and University of North Carolina were not even physically independent, let alone in any other way.

A few days later, Congress became involved when Sen. Jim Inhofe (R-Okla.) wrote to Sen. Barbara Boxer (D-Calif.), then chairman of the Senate Committee on Environment and Public Works, which was responsible for overseeing the EPA:[95]

Dear Senator Boxer,

It has come to my attention that the Environmental Protection Agency was recently sued in federal court for allegedly conducting illegal human experiments. A copy of the complaint is attached.

As I understand from the complaint, the EPA exposed dozens of human subjects, many of whom were health-impaired (e.g., asthma, metabolic syndrome, elderly) to concentrated high levels of substances like fine particulate mater (PM2.5) and diesel exhaust, which EPA has previously and officially determined can kill people and cause cancer.

It also appears that the EPA researchers failed to inform the Institutional Review Board and the study subjects of its official views concerning the lethality and toxicity of PM2.5 and diesel exhaust.

Keeping in mind the June 2005 report prepared for you and Rep. Henry Waxman entitled "Human Pesticide Experiments," the EPA's conduct may violate the laws, regulations and ethical standards set for the protection of human subjects. Indeed, the EPA may be criminally liable for its conduct.

As Ranking Member of the Senate Committee responsible for EPA oversight, I request that we conduct hearings on this matter in the upcoming "lame-duck" session.

Sincerely,

James M. Inhofe
Ranking Member
Committee on Environment and Public Works
U.S. Senate

Aside from Sen. Inhofe suggesting to Boxer that the EPA had acted criminally, he also raised Boxer's earlier foray into EPA human experiments, which occurred when the EPA was the responsibility of President George W. Bush.

In a report prepared by a joint House-Senate team for Sen. Boxer and Rep. Henry Waxman (D-Calif.), the Bush administration EPA was assailed, in part, for the following:[96]

> *In one experiment, human subjects were placed in a chamber with vapors of chloropicrin, an active ingredient in tear gas, at levels substantially higher that federal exposure limits.*

This, of course, was precisely what the EPA did with human study subjects and PM2.5, except that the EPA had determined that PM2.5 was much more dangerous than the tear gas ingredient.

Boxer's report went on to criticize the EPA concerning informed consent:

> *The informed consent forms used in the experiments do not appear to meet ethical standards. Some . . . failed to disclose the potential risks involved. One experiment exposed subjects to dimethoate, a pesticide that EPA considers a suspected carcinogen, a developmental toxicant and a neurotoxicant. Yet the informed consent form failed to mention these or any other potential health effects, stating instead that the chemical is "used to protect or cure all kinds of plants" and that "not a single health effect is expected."*

These were precisely the two main issues I had raised with the EPA Inspector General back in May 2012. But I received no response from Sen. Boxer who was copied on the complaint to the EPA Inspector General. Sen. Inhofe received no response from her on his letter, either.

CHAPTER 17

The EPA Admits to Junk Science

The EPA responded to the motion for a temporary restraining order on October 5, 2012. As expected, the EPA's first defense was that the court lacked the jurisdiction to hear the case because we had failed to identify a "final agency action" subject to review under the Administrative Procedures Act, the law general law governing the conduct of federal agencies. The EPA's second defense was that the allegations in our complaint were false. Lastly, the EPA claimed that we had suffered no irreparable harm and that an injunction against the experiments was not in the public interest.

But the most interesting part of the EPA's defense claims was its descriptions of and explanation for its human experiments.

First, the EPA's PM2.5 experiments were not limited to its facility at the University of North Carolina. The EPA revealed in its documents that similar experiments had also been conducted at a number of universities including the University of Michigan, the University of Washington, the University of Rochester, the University of Southern California and Rutgers University.

The EPA stated its reason for conducting the experiments as follows:[97]

These studies help to determine whether the mathematical associations between ambient (outdoor) levels of air pollutants and health effects seen in large-scale epidemiological studies are biologically plausible (or are not). They help to determine the mechanisms by which air pollutants cause adverse effects, whether certain people are more or less susceptible to exposure to air pollutants and (for PM2.5) whether certain chemical types are responsible (or not) for adverse effects.

But had not the EPA already regulated PM2.5 as if the epidemiological studies were biologically plausible since 1997? Recall that EPA chief Lisa Jackson had testified to Congress in 2011 that:

Particulate matter causes premature death. It doesn't make you sick. It's directly causal to dying sooner than you should.

None of the EPA's claims or conduct had exhibited any uncertainty as to whether PM2.5 was deadly. Its statement to the court was the diametric opposite of what it told the public about and how it regulated, PM2.5.

The EPA's defense continued:

This controlled exposure research provides information that cannot be obtained from large-scale epidemiological studies. Epidemiological studies, the primary tool in the discovery of risks to public health presented by ambient PM2.5, typically use data from large populations of people with varying susceptibility to PM2.5. They evaluate the relationship between changes in ambient levels of PM2.5 and changes in health effects. However epidemiological studies do not generally provide direct evidence of causation; instead they indicate the existence or absence of a statistical relationship. Large population studies cannot assess the biological mechanisms that could explain how inhaling ambient air pollution particles can cause illness or death in susceptible individuals.

So just in case the judge did not understand the EPA the first time about the inadequacy of epidemiologic studies for proving anything at all by themselves, the EPA reiterated that fact, hoping to underscore the importance of and need for its human experiments. Apparently since the people "dying" in the epidemiologic studies were merely statistical in nature, EPA wanted to prove the studies valid by creating some dead bodies of its own. But trying to harm or kill people for the sake advancing EPA science is not permitted.

The EPA's attempted defense against our allegations on informed consent was as follows:

> *EPA's regulations implementing the Common Rule require that all human participants of research studies provide their informed consent. The informed consent regulations require that participants be informed of "any reasonably foreseeable risks or discomforts <u>to the subject</u>" that may result from participation in the study.*
>
> *The regulations do not require a description of the more generalized risks to the public at large posed by the subject matter of the study. Indeed, as explained above with respect to PM2.5, the risks to a healthy individual from a time-limited, though concentrated, exposure are wholly distinct from the larger societal risks, which include especially vulnerable populations . . .*
>
> *Although the regulations do not require an explanation of the larger societal risks associated with PM2.5, participants are told that everyone is exposed to PM continuously in daily life and that such exposure has been associated with increased illness and death.*

The EPA tried to excuse itself from its failure to warn study subjects that PM2.5 was deadly because, the agency maintained,

PM2.5 was only deadly on a population basis, not an individual basis—as if populations are not comprised of individuals.

Then the EPA stated, "participants are told that everyone is exposed to PM continuously in daily life and that such exposure has been associated with increased illness and death." But as the EPA admits in its documents, the consent forms used in the CAPTAIN study only disclosed to the study subjects that:

> *During the exposure to the concentrated air pollution particles, you may experience some minor degree of airway irritation, cough and shortness of breath or wheezing. These symptoms typically disappear 2 to 4 hours after exposure, but may last longer for particularly sensitive people . . . Air pollution particles may induce an inflammatory reaction that can last for 24 hours after exposure and may increase the chance of you catching a cold.*

So where is the disclosure that "everyone is exposed to PM continuously in daily life and that such exposure has been associated with increased illness and death?" It was plainly not in the required consent form. The EPA goes on to conclude that:

> *Participants are given ample opportunity to ask questions about all of this during the interview process and they can end their participation at any time. This process fully and fairly satisfies the requirements for informed consent . . . ATI has not and cannot demonstrate that the EPA's informed consent procedures are deficient.*

But how can the study subjects ask about something—like the risk of death—that they have no idea is even a possibility? This will actually become a key point later in the story.

The EPA defended itself by claiming that the CAPTAIN experiments involved only "minimal risk," the disclosure of which was not required by the Common Rule. The EPA addressed this issue as follows:

The participants in the CAPTAIN study are not exposed to more than minimal risk. 'Minimal risk' is defined as 'the probability and magnitude of harm or discomfort anticipated in the research are not greater in and of themselves than those ordinarily encountered in daily life or during the performance of routine physical or psychological examinations or tests.' As explained above, CAPTAIN study participants are exposed to PM2.5 drawn from the air surrounding the test building in Chapel Hill, North Carolina. On a mass dose basis, particle concentrations 'will not exceed an exposure an individual receives over a 24-hour period while visiting a typical urban center in America on a smoggy day.' Under the study protocol, the concentration of inhaled particle mass to which participants are exposed cannot exceed 600 [millionths-of-a-gram per cubic meter] for more than a few minutes during a two-hour period. Exposure will be terminated within six minutes if concentrations exceed 600 [millionths-of-a-gram per cubic meter]. In fact, study participants are exposed to far lower concentrations than authorized by the study protocol, which calls for dilution of air entering the study chamber when the concentration of particles is measured at 500 millionths-of-a-gram per cubic meter in any two-minute average.

As a result, the PM2.5 concentrations to which the CAPTAIN participants have been exposed are well within expected exposure levels in their normal day-to-day life. The average dose of PM received by these subjects is 238.25 millionths-of-a-gram per cubic meter. This concentration is equivalent to experiencing a concentration of 19.85 millionths-of-a-gram per cubic meter over a 24-hour period, far less than the level of the 24-hour PM2.5 [regulatory standard of 35 millionths-of-a-gram]- Although the possibility of adverse effects can never be completely

> *ruled out, the risk posed to participants from exposure to PM2.5 in the CAPTAIN study "is very small." While there is a risk of a serious impact on public health when a large population (tens of millions) containing people with significant risk factors such as cardiovascular disease is exposed to elevated ambient levels of PM2.5, the risk of a serious effect to any one person exposed to PM2.5 concentrations for a period of two hours under the controlled conditions of the CAPTAIN study is very small, especially since EPA excludes participants from the CAPTAIN study – or any controlled human exposure study of PM2.5—who have significant risk factors for experiencing adverse effects to PM2.5.*

But nowhere in America does anyone inhale 600 or even 238.25 millionths-of-a-gram of PM2.5 in regular outdoor air at any moment. EPA dodged this dose issue by averaging out the PM2.5 chamber exposure over an entire 24-hour period. But outdoor air violates the EPA standard for "safe" PM2.5 and is virtually presumed to be dangerous the moment an air monitor measures 35 millionths-of-a-gram per cubic meter. A PM2.5 exposure of 600 millionths-of-a-gram per cubic meter is 17 times greater than the standard and is, by regulation, presumed to be dangerous to health. Moreover, the initial EPA documents that were obtained via the Freedom of Information Act about the experiments show that actual PM2.5 chamber exposures could reach 750 millionths-of-a-gram per cubic meter—more than 21 times greater than the EPA 24-hour standard.

The EPA again injected the bogus notion that PM2.5 doesn't kill individuals—just people in the population. The EPA further explained that these population victims are vulnerable to the effects of PM2.5. This completely ignores the reality that the EPA was experimenting on the very individuals who it says define "vulnerable groups"—those with metabolic syndrome, asthmatics and the elderly.

The EPA then argued that federal regulations allowed it to risk lives in order to enhance the agency's knowledge about PM2.5.

When conducting investigations pursuant to its statutory mandate, EPA is required to take into consideration 'the risks to the subjects, the adequacy of protection against these risks, the potential benefits of the research to the subjects and others and the importance of the knowledge gained or to be gained.' As discussed above, the risk to the participants in the CAPTAIN study is minimal, but the potential importance of the knowledge to be gained is not. Studies such as CAPTAIN provide EPA with knowledge about how $PM_{2.5}$ and its components affect human physiology and how particular genetic traits can impact this effect. Epidemiological studies simply cannot perform this function. Therefore, the minimal risk to participants in the study is not unreasonable on an individual level and is clearly justified by the importance of the knowledge that can be gained. [The American Tradition Institute's] claims, therefore, must fail. ATI argues that EPA may not consider this important knowledge as a benefit and suggests that human research may only be approved if it provides some anticipated benefit to the participant. But the regulatory language is directly to the contrary. [The Common Rule] requires that the IRB determine that 'risks to the subjects are reasonable in relation to anticipated benefits, if any, to subjects and the importance of the knowledge that may reasonably be expected to result.' This regulation refutes ATI's claim in two ways. First, the phrase 'if any' modifies the phrase 'anticipated benefits,' and thus specifically contemplates that a study may not have a direct benefit to the participant. EPA consent forms clearly explain when a study has no benefit to the participant (with the exception of monetary benefit and a medical examination). Second and more critically, the regulation also directs that the reasonableness of the risk be evaluated in light of 'the importance of the knowledge that may reasonably be expected to result.' This plainly allows approval of studies that present risks even when there are no direct benefits to the participant.*

Yet the EPA already regulated PM2.5 to the maximum level it believed it could. Moreover, it had already declared that there was no safe level of PM2.5 in outdoor air. So what, then, is the potential benefit of these experiments? That they prove to EPA that PM2.5 actually does kill?

Furthermore, the EPA's representation to the court that the Common Rule allows the Institutional Review Board to consider the importance of the knowledge willfully ignores what the Common Rule actually says.

Note how the EPA couches the societal benefit of its experiments in term of the "importance of the knowledge that may be reasonably be expected to result." But what does the Common Rule actually state? It says that the risks to study subjects must be:

> . . . *reasonable in relation to anticipated benefits, if any, to subjects and the importance of the knowledge that may reasonably be expected to result. In evaluating risks and benefits, the IRB should consider only those risks and benefits that may result from the research (as distinguished from risks and benefits of therapies subjects would receive even if not participating in the research). The IRB should not consider possible long-range effects of applying knowledge gained in the research (for example, the possible effects of the research on public policy) as among those research risks that fall within the purview of its responsibility.* [Emphasis added]

So, in fact, the Common Rule specifically bars the EPA from considering the benefits of the research to its regulatory programs.

Lastly, the EPA doubled down on the absurd distinction between individuals and populations.

> *As described above, participants in the CAPTAIN study are not exposed to more than minimal risk. If there is no more than minimal risk, there is certainly no risk of substantial*

114

injury. There are serious public health risks from exposure of large populations of people, including those with pre-existing illnesses, to ambient levels of PM2.5. But these are not the same as the very small risks that individuals who do not have such conditions face when volunteering to participate in a controlled study. While ATI asserts that 'EPA believes there is no safe level of PM2.5', that is not an accurate representation of EPA's position. Current standards for PM2.5 are based primarily on epidemiological studies. EPA has explained setting such standards is 'complicated by the recognition that no population threshold, below which it can be concluded with confidence that PM2.5-related effects do not occur, can be discerned from the available evidence.' Again, these statements are made in the context of "population" level risks and do not reflect individual risks. If anything, this uncertainty emphasizes the need for controlled human exposure studies to increase the body of knowledge. Because the state of the science regarding PM2.5 is not complete, it is important that EPA conduct research to better understand how PM2.5 affects people and what particular human characteristics might impact the likelihood of an adverse reaction to it.

Here the EPA denies in one sentence that there is "no safe level of PM2.5" but then embraces in the next sentence the notion there is no safe level of PM2.5 on a population basis—once again, as if populations are not made up of individuals.

In addition to the EPA's memorandum laying out its defenses, the agency also submitted to the court other documents including statements or declarations from individuals on behalf of the EPA and the CAPTAIN documents, including the Institutional Review Board application and consent form. The declaration of one Martin W. Case was amazing.

Mr. Case declared to the court that he was the "clinical research studies coordinator" for the CAPTAIN study. His job was to do the training, testing, monitoring and coordinating for EPA's human clinical studies. He then goes on to describe his presentation of the CAPTAIN study to the human study subjects. He describes the end of his presentations to study subjects as follows:[98]

> *Finally, I assure them of our concern for their safety first and foremost. Specifically, I tell them of the safe guards we have in place for monitoring their vitals signs, (e.g. EKG telemetry, blood pressure and oxygen saturation; 'especially while in the chamber'). I show the subject that they are always on camera, that they can just speak up to be heard and that I am always just several feet away at the console watching them. As I am performing the training, I physically show them the controlled testing chambers and point out all of these features and safe guards that we have in place. In addition, I informed them of our emergency medical equipment, our overhead paging capability, immediate emergency response by our nurses and that a dedicated on-call physician is always in the facility at all times when any study is taking place. I state again, 'Any questions?'.*
>
> *I provide participants with information about fine particles (PM2.5). I say that PM2.5 are particles so small that they are able past through your airways and go deep into your lungs, these particles are so small that your usual lining and cilia of your airways are not able to prevent these particles from passing into your lungs, Therefore, if you are a person that for example lives in a large city like Los Angeles or New York and it's been a very hot day and you can see the haze in the air and you happen to be someone that works outside and if you have an underlying unknown health condition, or, you may be older in age; the chances are that you could end up in the emergency room later on that night, wondering what's wrong, possibly having cardiac changes that could lead to a heart attack; there is the possibility you may die from this.*

I make sure they have initialed and dated every page of the consent form, printed and signed their name in the proper place and correctly dated the consent. I in turn do the same as the person obtaining their consent. I file this copy in their study chart and I also make sure they have a signed identical copy to take with them as reference, with contact telephone numbers of the PI, study personnel, our EPA approval medical officer (who oversees our research protocols) and the telephone number with contact information for the Internal Review Board of the University of North Carolina at Chapel Hill who oversees and approves this and all of our studies.

So Case claims that he told the human study subjects in the CAPTAIN study that,

There is the possibility you may die from this.

Yet the EPA's defense states the opposite.

The EPA repeatedly told the court that the risk of death did not apply to individuals but only to populations. Case's statement would seem to shatter that claim since Case informed each study subject that "you may die" from PM2.5. Although Case's statement is made in the context of a hypothetical vulnerable person in Los Angeles or New York on a bad air day, recall that the EPA consent forms presented earlier liken the chamber exposure to PM2.5 like a bad air day in those cities. Also, as the EPA's human study subjects are selected for experimentation both for their vulnerable status, that is either or both health-compromised and elderly, Case's "there is the possibility you may die from this" statement clearly meant to apply to the chamber exposure.

Next, there is the EPA's claim that the chamber exposure to PM2.5 amounted to only "minimal risk." Then why mention it at all as "minimal risks" do not need to be disclosed. It would seem to be poor salesmanship for a recruiter to tell a potential study subject compensated at a rate of $12 per hour that, "there is a possibility you may die from this."

Recall that the EPA's defense against the claim of deficient informed consent was:

> *Participants are given ample opportunity to ask questions about all of this during the interview process and they can end their participation at any time This process fully and fairly satisfies the requirements for informed consent . . . ATI has not and cannot demonstrate that EPA's informed consent procedures are deficient.*

Except that, as death cannot possibly be considered to be "minimal risk," and written, as opposed to oral, consent is required by the Common Rule when risks to study subjects exceed minimal risk, a glib oral mention to study subjects that they may die from the experiment runs far afoul of federal regulations.[99]

What we learned here was that the EPA was willing to say anything to anyone to get what it wanted. If the EPA wanted more regulation then, PM2.5 could kill people on a near instantaneous basis. If the EPA wanted to not be liable for conducting experiments on vulnerable people, then PM2.5 was harmless. As pointed out in the Washington Times op-ed, the EPA was misleading someone.

CHAPTER 18

EPA's 'Get out of the Nuremberg Code FREE' Card

The EPA was accused of experimenting on real, live humans with what the agency had previously determined was a lethal substance. This violated every rule for the protection of human subject in scientific research that had been established since World War II. Yet the U.S. District Court for the Eastern District of Virginia – Alexandria Division was oddly more focused on nitpicking civil procedure than the merits of the case.

What follows is from the transcript of the October 9, 2012:[100]

> *THE COURT: This case is before the Court on an application for a temporary restraining order by the plaintiffs. The Court has reviewed the complaint, the motion memoranda and the opposition of the EPA.*
>
> *Let me hear first from the plaintiff. I'll be happy to hear anything you don't think you've already adequately explained to the Court. I'd like you to concentrate, though, on the points raised in the defendant's opposition, particularly the subject matter jurisdiction issue.*

MR. SCHNARE: Thank you, Your Honor. I had nine pages. I think I'm down to one now.

THE COURT: Well, I'll give you an opportunity to say what you'd like, but if you would, focus on the jurisdictional issue.

MR. SCHNARE: Yes, Your Honor. The jurisdictional issue deals with, in essence, whether or not there is a final agency action at issue. The final agency action [in this case] is not a regulatory action. We're not talking about challenging a regulation here. Instead, Your Honor, we're talking about a contract that the agency has made between itself and 6—so far 6 subjects and up to 30 they intend to do [experiments on].

THE COURT: Why is that within the scope of [Administrative Procedures Act]?

MR. SCHNARE: Because the law that is at issue here is the informed consent law, what's known as the Common Rule. There's no judicial review opportunity within that rule or within that law or within those regulations. The [Administrative Procedures Act] thus allows for a review, a judicial review of something otherwise not subject to judicial review. It is a final agency action under the Bennett rule, Your Honor, because that contract between these people and the agency creates legal rights in those individuals and those legal rights have been abrogated to the degree that these folks have failed to properly inform them of the risk of death and the risk of exposure to carcinogens.

THE COURT: Well, you say the Common Rule. What is it about the Common Rule that you're challenging?

MR. SCHNARE: The Common Rule requires that there be informed consent and it requires that the Institutional Review

Board, which reviews human studies, be fully informed before the study takes place and before they enter into an agreement with these human subjects. It is our contention and the facts show and the EPA admissions demonstrate that the agency never informed these individuals in writing that they had a risk of death. They said that they said so verbally. In one of the declarations, the EPA said, if you—that there is a possibility you may die from this. But that's not written down in the informed consent. It's required to be there.

THE COURT: I know the government has chosen not to defend on this basis, but why is there—why do your clients have standing to raise that issue if this is a lack of informed consent issue, which is what I hear you saying? Why isn't that simply a claim that these individuals could make under the appropriate procedural mechanism?

MR. SCHNARE: [EPA is] imposing an unreasonable risk by exposing them to cancer and a carcinogenic study. Of course, there is the whole risk of death. The administrator of the agency says that one in four people die of this every year.

THE COURT: So you're claiming that the risk that these people are exposed to violates the Common Rule and that would be the case even in the presence of informed consent?

MR. SCHNARE: That's correct, Your Honor.

THE COURT: All right.

MR. SCHNARE: Do you want me to go—well, there are four elements to a [temporary restraining order requirement]. Do you want to go over those or not?

THE COURT: I'm, again, unclear on why this would fall within the scope of review under the [Administrative Procedures Act].

Our argument closed with:

If you look at the Reference Manual on Scientific Evidence, Third Edition, which just came out last year, Your Honor—this is written by the Federal Judicial Center and the National Research Council—they state in there in the section on epidemiology, 'When an agent's affects are suspected to be harmful, researchers cannot knowingly expose people to the agent.' That's the law. That's been well-recognized for a long time. The EPA entered a moral hazard. It failed to realize it had a moral hazard and it went forward in any case. It is putting people at risk that don't belong at risk. It need not do it because the agency has no value added from this because the regulatory process is already well underway.

I would also add, Your Honor, that the medical board for North Carolina has initiated an investigation of this matter. They have informed us in three different letters that that investigation continues and that it won't be concluded for up to six months. The dean of the medical school who owns, if you will, organizes the Institutional Review Board has initiated a review as well.

So these reviews are going to be ongoing. The question is should you continue to expose people to carcinogens and put them at risk of death while those reviews are going on. We believe they should not, Your Honor.

THE COURT: Thank you. Let me hear from the EPA.

The EPA then proceeded through its defense, making the points previously highlighted. A notable point that always bears repeating was the EPA's disavowal of the PM2.5 epidemiologic studies:

What we get from the epidemiological studies shows the long-term impacts on a large population. What is missing is the detailed information to show a cause-and-effect relationship for exposure to PM2.5 with health effects and the biological plausibility, the likelihood that these health effects may happen. Very important information not only for EPA in establishing its public policy and establishing regulations, but that also provides part of the scientific database that other researchers rely upon in finding what diseases are caused and maybe even leading to cures. Those are important pieces of scientific information that can only come from doing the controlled human exposure studies.

So while the EPA relies on the PM2.5 epidemiology to impose expensive regulations on the economy, it simultaneously dismisses that very epidemiology in a court of law to justify its human experiments.

After about an hour of back-and-forth oral argument, the Court denied our request for a temporary restraining order. The EPA's double talk convinced him that there was no imminent harm to anyone. Satisfied on that subject, he then cited the American Tradition Institute's lack of standing to raise these matters in the first place. That wasn't the end, however.

We were back in court four months later to argue the jurisdictional issue. While that hearing did not touch directly on the science of PM2.5, it was notable for the general arrogance of the EPA. In its brief to the court for that hearing, the EPA stated:[101]

The EPA's Decision to Study PM2.5 with Human Participants Is a Decision Committed to Agency Discretion by Law.
. . . Nothing in the [Clean Air Act] provides a meaningful standard to evaluate what air pollution the EPA chooses to study or how.
Because 'no judicially manageable standards are available for judging how and when [the EPA] should exercise its dis-

cretion' in deciding what research to undertake, the EPA's decision to study the health effects of PM2.5 using controlled human exposure studies was a decision committed to the EPA's discretion and immune from review under the APA.

So the EPA's position was that its human research program was essentially above the law—and that's eventually how the Court saw it, too. On January 31, 2013, our lawsuit was dismissed on the basis that the American Tradition Institute lacked the requisite legal standing to bring the case so, in turn, the court lacked the jurisdiction to hear it.

In a follow-up commentary in the *Washington Times*, I wrote:

It's a good thing the U.S Public Health Service called off the infamous Tuskegee syphilis experiments in 1972. Had someone sued to stop the horror, a federal judge like the Anthony Trenga might have stopped the suit—not the experiments.

That's precisely what Judge Trenga did on Jan. 31 in the case of the American Tradition Institute (ATI) v. U.S. Environmental Protection Agency (EPA).

ATI sued the EPA in October to stop an ongoing experiment in which the agency was exposing elderly study subjects (up to 75 years of age) to concentrated levels of a deadly (according to EPA) air pollutant known as PM2.5 (soot or dust much smaller than the width of a human hair).

The lawsuit claimed the experiments were illegal in that they blatantly violated virtually every major standard developed since World War II for the protection of human study subjects used in scientific experiments.

Given that the EPA long ago determined that any exposure to PM2.5 could cause death (as well as a host of other serious health consequences) within hours or days of inhalation, the experiments are fundamentally illegal. Federal regulations and the Nuremberg Code strictly prohibit scientists from treating human subjects like expendable guinea pigs. In the experiment in question, the study subjects were asked to risk their very lives for $12 per hour.

But then the study subjects really weren't "asked" to risk their lives since the EPA researchers failed—and, in fact, refused to warn them that PM2.5 could kill them. At the very least, exposing study subjects to a dangerous and deadly toxin without their consent is also known as 'assault and battery.'

But to Judge Trenga, the important thing apparently was to nitpick to death the effort to stop the experiments with a narrow reading of the federal rules of civil procedure.

Judge Trenga determined that the EPA's decision to endanger the lives of its study subjects, including inducing them to a fraudulent consent form, didn't constitute a 'final agency action' under the Administrative Procedures Act. Judge Trenga also determined, as ATI was not being harmed by the experiments, it didn't have standing to pursue the case.

Presumably Judge Trenga might have allowed an actual human study subject to maintain a lawsuit to stop the experiments, but then again, how would they? The EPA lied to each of them about the risks of the experiment.

But lifetime-appointed and, hence, unaccountable Judge Trenga essentially decided, in agreement with Department of Justice and EPA pleadings, that no one and no law can stop the EPA from breaking the sacrosanct rules protecting human subjects from rogue experimentation. His ruling came despite the fact that the federal rules of civil procedure explicitly state that they 'must be construed so as to do justice.'

Thanks to Judge Trenga, EPA (and possibly any other rogue government human experimenter) now has a 'GET OUT OF THE NUREMBERG CODE FREE' card.

Perhaps looking for a way to wash his hands of the case, Judge Trenga did ask ATI during the hearing whether a political solution was being sought against the EPA experiments.

And yes, the House has asked the EPA Office of the Inspector General (IG) to investigate and Sen. Jim Inhofe (R-Okla.) asked Senate Environment and Public Works Committee chairman Barbara Boxer to hold hearings last October.

But aside from the high probability of a whitewash by the EPA IG and Sen. Boxer's failure to take any action so far, the experiments are ongoing and the study subjects are in mortal danger now. Moreover, it doesn't seem reasonable to expect expedited, or even any political action from a polarized Congress that hasn't passed a basic budget for the country in years.

Consider that Supreme Court Justice John Roberts recently had no qualms about distending the Constitution to compel people to buy health insurance under Obamacare. But federal district court Judge Trenga wasn't even willing to at least temporarily liberalize his interpretation of the federal rules of civil procedure so that he could at least hear all the facts in the human testing case.

The EPA's guinea pigs didn't get any 'compassionate conservatism' from this appointee of George W. Bush—of course, they still don't even know they are being treated like lab rats.

Despite the unfortunate ruling by Judge Trenga, this controversy is not over—not by a long shot. The effort to spotlight and stop the EPA's outrageous conduct will continue. But don't expect it to be easy.

When I broke the news of the EPA's misconduct in this column last April, I noted that in conducting these experiments, the EPA either lied to the study subjects (giving rise to civil and possibly criminal liability) or the agency lied to Congress and the public about the dangers of PM2.5 (risking the agency's reputation and related regulatory programs). That question remains of great import.

It's just too bad Judge Trenga wasn't interested in learning the answer.

This legal setback had been proceeded a day earlier by final action from the North Carolina Medical Board on my complaint concerning the EPA physicians involved in the OMEGACON study that sent the 58-year-old woman to the hospital with a cardiac arrhythmia.

Back in October 2012, the North Carolina Medical Board had dismissed my complaint against Dr. Eugene Chung, one of the physicians involved in the incident with the 58-year-old woman. Though the notice of that dismissal provided no explanation of why Chung was let off the hook, a media contact told me the Board had determined that Chung was not involved in the EPA experiment, but only in treating her at the hospital afterward.

But as the Board's explanation wasn't entirely irrational, it just seemed to be an indication of the Board conducting a bona fide investigation. But then in late January, the Board notified me that it was concluding its investigation without taking any action. The Board wrote without further explanation:

> *While we know you may not agree with the decision, you can be sure it was reached after a fair and thorough evaluation.*

It's not clear how "fair" any of this actually was. Six of the Board's 12 members had either attended or worked for the University of North Carolina and another Board member was a state political appointee. None of these people would tend to have an interest in drawing unfavorable attention to the state school or jeopardizing the school's multi-million dollar the EPA gravy train.[102]

The outcomes of the lawsuit and North Carolina Medical Board "investigation" were both disappointing, but then again, neither outcome had been decided by an open and thorough vetting of the facts. And besides, there was more to come.

CHAPTER 19

Killer Air Pollution Research

During the period of the trial, I finally discovered someone who had been killed by air pollution—or more accurately government-funded air pollution human experimentation. I had been in contact with a walking-talking encyclopedia on human experimentation, Vera Sharav, a Holocaust survivor who was also founder and president of the Alliance for Human Research Protection. Sharav said she remembered a college-aged woman who died while participating in clinical air pollution experiments during the 1990s.

That poor woman turned out to be 19-year-old Hoiyan (Nicole) Wan who had volunteered for a National Institute of Environmental Health Sciences-funded experiment at the University of Rochester on the role of airborne chemicals in lung cancer. This was not an EPA-sponsored experiment but it was done for the purposes of developing science for EPA air quality regulations.

Wan had been accidentally overdosed with the topical anesthetic lidocaine during a bronchoscopy, a procedure involving the insertion of a flexible tube down the trachea in order to biopsy the lower portion of the lung. Too much lidocaine was used to suppress her gag reflex and Wan developed breathing problems. She was admitted to the hospital where she died two days later.[103] Wan's family sued and settled for a "reasonable" but undisclosed financial settlement, plus a small scholarship in Wan's name and a lecture series.

The tragedy was notable on three levels. First, the experiment was absolutely ridiculous and unethical. Were the researchers intent on trying to cause lung cancer in the study subjects? What possible useful information about cancer could they get from briefly exposing someone to a chemical and then biopsying the lung? Sorry, but that is not how cancer works. If nothing else, it is common knowledge that smokers only get lung cancer after decades of heavy smoking. One experimental inhalation just won't do it or provide any meaningful indication that lung cancer is even a possibility.

Second, documents showed that the EPA was performing bronchoscopies on some of its human subjects. Certainly bronchoscopies are typically a safe procedure when performed properly. But when the procedure is undertaken, it is usually for some specific medical purpose or benefit—as opposed to merely helping the government formulate public policy. Remember that, under the Common Rule, potential use in public policy is not a valid benefit to be considered by an Institutional Review Board in deciding whether to approve a human experiment.

Finally, the tragedy didn't seem to have any sobering effect on the University of Rochester. The university opposed legislation advocated by Wan's parents requiring notification of parents when students under the age of 21 participate in medical experiments. University provost Charles Phelps wrote in to the school newspaper that:[104]

> *There are lots of things that students do to put them at risk [including drinking, unprotected sex and recreational drug use]. . . In medical experiments, the satisfaction is the money and the knowledge that you're contributing to the body of scientific knowledge. I see no reason to interfere in the students' autonomy.*

University President Thomas Jackson attempted to polish the University of Rochester image by portraying Wan as a hero rather than a victim:[105]

*[Wan's death] occurred following her willing participation in
support of one of the basic missions of the university—research
that will enable individuals to live better.*

Yes, who wouldn't want to sacrifice their life for the sake of the
government regulation?

While Wan paid the ultimate price for her sacrifice, the University
of Rochester suffered no significant consequences. In fact, the
university has since collected from the EPA since 2000 nearly $20
million in additional grants for human experiments involving
particulate matter. The researchers responsible for overseeing
the experiment that resulted in Wan's death were not disciplined, but instead have since profited from the EPA's grants
to the university.

Shortly after learning of the Wan tragedy, news came that the
EPA Inspector General had agreed to investigate the agency's human
experimentation. But that had required the involvement of Congress.

Staff members of the House Space, Science and Technology
Committee had been in contact with the Inspector General and had
negotiated a deal for the investigation. This saved the EPA Inspector
General of the apparent embarrassment of having to
respond to my request.

Back on October 18, 2012, Rep. Paul Broun, a physician and
chairman of the Science Committee's Subcommittee on Investigations
and Oversight wrote to the EPA Inspector General, formally requesting an investigation.[106] The inspector general's written response
agreeing to investigate came in kabuki-like fashion a mere four days
later without fanfare.[107]

Despite all the attention being placed on the EPA's PM2.5 human
experimentation program, the agency continued almost unabated.[108]
In mid-December 2012, the EPA once again tightened its standards
for PM2.5 in outdoor air, this time lowering its annual average for
PM2.5 from 15 down to 12 millionths-of-a-gram per cubic centi-
meter of air.[109]

In the rule as published in the *Federal Register*, EPA offered this explanation of why its experiments on humans with PM2.5 don't jibe with its claims about the PM2.5 epidemiology:[110]

> *The EPA disagrees with commenters that the mild and reversible effects observed in controlled human exposure studies are inconsistent with the more serious effects observed in epidemiological studies. Ethical considerations regarding the types of studies that can be performed with human subjects generally limit the effects that can be evaluated to those that are transient, reversible and of limited short-term consequence. The relatively small number of subjects recruited for controlled exposure studies should also be expected to have less variability in health status and risk factors than occurring in the general population. Consequently, the severity of health effects observed in controlled human exposure studies evaluating the effects of PM should be expected to be less than observed in epidemiologic studies. Nonetheless, that effects are observed in relatively healthy individuals participating in controlled exposure studies serves as an indicator that PM is initiating health responses and that more severe responses may reasonably be expected in a more diverse population.*

So EPA offers three defenses for the disparity between the results of the PM2.5 human experiments and the epidemiology. First, EPA claims it limits its experiments to testing for health effects that are "transient, reversible and of limited short-term consequence." Except that EPA Administrator Lisa Jackson testified to Congress that,

> *Particulate matter causes premature death. It doesn't make you sick. It's directly causal to dying sooner than you should.*

And there is nothing about death that is "transient, reversible or of limited short-term consequence."

Next EPA maintains that its human experiments have too few study subjects to represent the variability of the human population. That is a clear admission that, in fact, these human experiments are of dubious scientific value especially with an eye toward regulations for the entire population. Pointless human experimentation runs afoul of the Common Rule as:[111]

> *Research means a systematic investigation, including research development, testing and evaluation, designed to develop or contribute to generalizable knowledge.*

Finally, the EPA states that the effects it has observed in its human study subjects may be extrapolated as much more serious consequences among the general population. But this claim is debunked by the EPA's own admission that it is limited to looking for "transient effects"—effects that by definition are short-lived after the exposure. Moreover, just because one experiences an effect following a stimulus—like some small physiological change in response to inhaling a high level of PM2.5 for two hours—that doesn't mean that the effect is necessarily harmful. To be sure, you will experience a physiological effect just from drinking a glass of water. But that mere effect is obviously not harmful.

The EPA also added a footnote to this passage explaining how it ensures that it is only experiments on healthy humans. This footnote reads, in relevant part:

> *The EPA excludes from its controlled human exposure studies involving exposure to PM2.5 any individual with a significant risk factor for experiencing adverse effects from such exposure.*

Except that the documents obtained via the Freedom of Information Act about the EPA experiments showed that the agency was recruiting for its experiments the sick and elderly, the precise people the agency claims are most vulnerable to PM2.5. Additionally, the lengthy footnote specifically mentions diabetes as reason for excluding someone from experimentation. Yet University of Rochester researchers dutifully reported back to EPA about a human experiment it conducted for the agency:[112]

> *We have completed our study of the effects of inhalation of ultrafine carbon particles in subjects with diabetes.*

There is clearly a disconnect at the EPA between those writing the rules and those conducting the experiments.

CHAPTER 20

EPA's Child Abuse

Though the EPA inspector general was supposed to have completed his investigation by April 2013, according to his agreement with Congress, that deadline came and went with no report. Meanwhile, the PM2.5 testing scandal only became more bizarre, if not frustrating.

I had discovered in December 2012 that EPA apparently had funded some sort of human testing at the University of Southern California (USC) involving PM2.5 from diesel exhaust sprayed up the noses of children. Naturally curious, I contacted the principal investigator at USC, one Frank Gilliland, writing:

> *Dr. Gilliland,*
>
> *I am working on an article about air pollution clinical studies.*
> *Can you tell me if your mid-2000s work with Phase II enzymes and children was ever published?*
>
> *Thanks,*
>
> *Steve Milloy*

Possibly my email was lost in the holiday rush. Possibly word was sent to EPA researchers to not interact with Steve Milloy. I don't know, but no response ever came from Gilliland. I tried again on January 8, 2013. Again, no response. So, on to Plan B.

Vera Sharav of the Alliance for Human Research Protection put me in contact with a public radio reporter named Kelley Weiss who was affiliated with the California Healthcare Foundation Center for Reporting, which was affiliated with the USC's Annenberg School of Communication and Journalism. Weiss and I talked on the phone and had a few e-mail exchanges. She claimed to have made some inquiries and subsequently sent me some irrelevant information. But she broke contact after a few days. While I don't know what happened, but it's quite possible that her affiliation with the USC had something to do with her deciding not to pursue the investigation of USC's Gilliland.

Just when discouragement was about to set in, the EPA came to the rescue. On February 25, I went back to the EPA database where I had found the report about the experiments with children. Although the report, or at least part of it, was still in the database, the section of the document describing the exposure of the children to diesel exhaust had been deleted.

This was not likely accidental as the EPA had been caught scrubbing from one of its online databases documents related to grants given to one Peter Gleick, president of the Oakland, California-based Pacific Institute. Gleick had been embarrassingly caught in a case of fraudulent impersonation for the purposes of obtaining confidential documents from the Heartland Institute, a Chicago-based think tank. The EPA had apparently deleted the documents to avoid being linked with the miscreant Gleick. I immediately filed a request under the Freedom of Information Act to find out what had happened to Gleick's grants. Magically, after my FOIA request and ensuing media uproar, Gleick's grants were restored to the EPA database.

So I filed another Freedom of Information Act request with the EPA, regarding the report about the testing of diesel exhaust on children. The EPA's response came two months later. It confirmed what I suspected had happened. The documents provided to me were a series of emails concerning the deletion. On the bright side, they confirmed that the deletion did, in fact occur and was highly unusual—the first deletion of its kind in 13 years. On the other hand, no one at the EPA could (or would) determine who or what had caused the deletion to occur. Still, one EPA manager expressed seemingly genuine concern:[113]

> *This situation is very disconcerting in that [EPA staff] as of yet has no idea what caused the problem to occur in the first place.*

I filed yet another Freedom of Information Act request asking for records associated with the diesel exhaust experiments on children in August of 2013. Multiple requests and more than a year later, a substantive response finally arrived. The information about the experiments was so outrageous, after being posted on JunkScience. com, it made the top of the Drudge Report.

The documents I received from the EPA, including Institutional Review Board applications and consent forms, showed that the EPA-funded researchers from USC and the University of California, Los Angeles (UCLA), had sprayed diesel exhaust up the noses of children 10 to 15 years of age.[114] The amount of diesel exhaust administered at one time amounted to as much as 300 millions of a gram of diesel exhaust, 95 percent of which is PM2.5, which the EPA characterized as two days worth of the PM2.5 in Los Angeles air. That dose of PM2.5 is 8.5 times greater than the maximum amount of PM2.5 allowed in outdoor air—and infinitely more than the level the EPA had previously told the public and Congress was safe, which was zero.

There was, of course, no benefit to the children from these experiments, although the EPA did have the nerve to tell them:

> *Your only benefit is that you may learn how well your body makes antioxidants in response to pollutants.*

Meanwhile, the EPA told the Institutional Review Board that the only health effect the children might experience from the experiment was some itching. The application stated:

> *Diesel is considered a toxic air contaminant in California and a likely carcinogen by the EPA. However, it is clear that its potential effects on cancer only come upon high-level lifetime exposures and not acute exposures. Indeed the EPA itself has given approval for its own scientists to do human diesel exposures. It should be stressed that concentrations used here mimic real world exposure levels. It is very important to realize that the cancer risk associated with diesel is solely for lung cancer. In this case following the nasal challenge, the amount that will reach the lung is extremely small; most is cleared by the nasal cilia in 48 hours or else swallowed and naturally excreted. In rare cases, subjects may experience an unpleasant taste like soot. Some itching may occur.*

In addition to the familiar failure to mention that EPA had determined any exposure to PM2.5 can kill people within hours of inhalation, the EPA-funded researchers' disclosure, such as it was, fell way short of the mark according to California standards set six years earlier.

At that time, the California Air Resources Board (CARB) released an assessment of diesel exhaust concluding that it can cause cancer and that there is no safe exposure to it:[115]

> *Based on scientific information, a level of diesel exhaust exposure below which no carcinogenic effects are anticipated has not been identified.*

But the California regulator, the California Air Resources Board (CARB), also concluded that:

138

A number of adverse short-term health effects have been associated with exposures to diesel exhaust. Occupational exposures to diesel exhaust have been associated with significant cross-shift decrease in lung function, increased cough, labored breathing, chest tightness and wheezing have been associated with exposure to diesel exhaust in garage workers. A significant increase in airway resistance and increases in eye and nasal irritation were observed in human volunteers following one-hour chamber exposure to diesel exhaust. In acute or subchronic animal studies, exposure to diesel exhaust particles induced inflammatory airway changes, lung function changes and increased the animals susceptibility to infection . . .

Studies have also shown that diesel exhaust particles can induce immunological reaction and localized inflammatory responses in humans, as well as acting as an adjuvant for pollen allergy . . .

So while the EPA tried to downplay any cancer risk from diesel exhaust exposure, there were plenty of other short-term non-cancer risks that should have been disclosed to participants, especially minors—if exposure to PM2.5 had actually represented any sort of actual risk to health.

Additionally, and referencing the EPA's own conclusions about diesel exhaust, the state of California also had concluded that the permissible level of diesel exhaust in air would be limited to 5 millionths-of-a-gram per cubic meter. As the EPA-funded experiments on the children entailed exposures of up to 300 millionths-of-a-gram, the experiments violated the California state standard by a factor of 60.

The experiments involved children as young as 10 years old supposedly because EPA believes children are more vulnerable to the effects of pollution. This is similar to the EPA's claim that the elderly and sick are more vulnerable. EPA justified using children in the experiment in the Institutional Review Board application as follows:

The whole rationale for this study is that while much work has been done on adults, pollution is thought to primarily affect children.

So whatever the health risks of concern were for adults, they would then have been even greater for children. But the EPA-funded researchers failed to provide complete disclosure on the adult risks, let alone these supposed increased risks to children.

Before leaving the topic of the EPA-funded diesel particulate experiments on children, there is one final notable aspect of it. The EPA proposed to ban experiments on children on May 7, 2003. The agency then actually banned such experiments on Jun 23, 2006.[116] But the EPA-funded experiments at USC, occurred in the interim period of 2004-2005. So at the very same time that the EPA was seeking to ban experiments on children, it was paying for such experiments to be conducted.

How then did these diesel exhaust experiments on children manage to evade the EPA's ban? The obvious answer—that the ban was only "proposed" at the time of the USC experiments—is probably not the correct one. The actual explanation is more likely that the actual aim of the EPA ban on child experimentation was aimed at pesticide manufacturers that might study real-life pesticide exposures in homes where children live. This was the topic that so animated Sen. Boxer and Rep. Waxman in 2005, as previously discussed.

Concerned that such studies tend to show that children are not dangerously exposed to pesticides when used according to directions in homes, pesticide opponents sought to extinguish the possibility that pesticide manufacturers could submit them to the EPA as evidence of product safety. This is the scenario that was the likely target of the ban. The EPA wasn't necessarily interested in banning its own scientists from doing child experiments that could be used to advance the cause of its regulatory agenda. But it did want to stop pesticide manufacturers from blocking that agenda.

CHAPTER 21

'No Safe Level'

The University of Southern California and the University of California, Los Angeles, weren't the only universities taking money from the EPA for human PM2.5 experiments. In October 2012, I questioned the University of Rochester about similar experiments by asking the university to suspend any ongoing testing pending an investigation and requesting copies of Institutional Review Board applications and consent forms.[117]

The university's general counsel responded a few days later, stating in relevant part:[118]

> Dear Mr. Milloy,
>
> Thank you for your letter of October 16. Our [Institutional Review Board] did review and approve the research you referenced. The [Institutional Review Board] will review it again, including research subject safety and relevant Institutional Review Board applications and study subject consent forms . . .
>
> Sincerely,
>
> Sue Stewart

Hoping for sincerity on the part of the University of Rochester's General Counsel, I immediately thanked her for replying promptly and sent her more information, including the news that Congress had requested that the EPA Inspector General investigate EPA's human experiments. I received the following reply:[119]

Dear Mr. Milloy,

This email is in response to your request for a status update . . . we have determined that there is only one study at the UR currently enrolling patients that would arguably fall within the scope of your concerns. We are undertaking a thorough re-review of that study, including obtaining comment from an independent consultant from outside the institution. The [Institutional Review Board] is proceeding expeditiously, but a good review will still take some time to complete.

In the interim, I want to let you know that University of Rochester excluded from eligibility for this research any people who because of pre-existing conditions might be vulnerable to research related injury.

Sue Stewart

I continued to send relevant information, including the news that the EPA Inspector General had agreed to Congress' request to investigate the agency's human experiments. I also renewed an earlier request for documents. Two months later in January 2013, I emailed the University of Rochester general counsel a Freedom of Information Act request for Institutional Review Board applications and consent forms. I was told to ask the EPA for the records.[120]

Four months later the University of Rochester sent me the following:[121]

Dear Mr. Milloy –

This is to provide you with the final results of our review in response to the concerns you brought to our attention regarding air pollution research conducted at the University of Rochester. Christine Burke, Medical Center General Counsel, asked me to communicate this information to you in her absence.

As you know, in order to reassess the propriety of the research at issue and to ensure objectivity we requested outside reviews by two independent experts unaffiliated with the University. The two experts are both board certified pulmonologists associated with major academic medical centers. They thoroughly reviewed the initial applications to the RSRB for approval of the research and the consent forms. They also consulted the applicable literature and relied upon their own knowledge and expertise in order to quantify the clinical risks involved in the research. Both experts concluded that the subjects were not exposed to undue risk, that the risks were appropriately disclosed and that the research was appropriate. We now consider this matter closed, although we do reserve the right to consider the conclusions of the EPA regarding the studies at issue when they are available. Thank you for bringing your concerns to our attention.

Spencer L. Studwell, Esq.
Associate Vice President for Risk Management.
Sr. Associate General Counsel
University of Rochester, Strong Memorial Hospital and Strong Health

Realizing that the University of Rochester "investigation" still didn't resolve any of the fundamental ethical issues involving risk and disclosure, I sent the EPA a Freedom of Information Act request for the documents about the experiments. Several months later the EPA responded with documents that revealed an experiment in which study subjects up to 60 years of age were exposed to PM2.5 at levels 10-20 times greater than in outdoor air.[122] Once again and contrary to EPA's public claims, inhaling concentrated levels of PM2.5 was no risk, even to asthmatics. The consent form stated, in relevant part:

> *It is very unlikely that these exposures to concentrated outdoor particles will cause symptoms or clinically important effects in healthy subjects. We have previously completing [sic] a study of [ultrafine particle] exposure in healthy subjects and in health subjects with asthma and there have been no symptoms or airway effects in those studies. The U.S. Environmental Protection Agency completed a study in healthy subjects using the same Harvard fine ultrafine particle concentrator and found no adverse effects. We previously exposed subjects with asthma to 10 millionths-of-a-gram per cubic meter laboratory-generated carbon ultrafine particles, with intermittent exercise, without symptoms or airway effects. Our previous studies of exposure to ultrafine particles at 50 millions of a gram per cubic meter, with intermittent exercise, were without adverse effects. This study will be conducted at rest, which will further reduce the particle dose. In a separate study . . . healthy subjects have been exposed to ultrafine and fine zinc oxide particles at a concentration of 500 millionths-of-a-gram per cubic meter without adverse effects. Previous human studies of exposure to fine carbon particles found no clinical effects of exposure to 250 millionths of a gram per cubic meter for 1 hour or 500 millionths-of-a-gram per cubic meter for 2 hours.*

This language was at odds with EPA's description of the health risks of PM2.5 in its December 2012 rule tightening the outdoor PM2.5 standard:

Several new studies have examined the association between cardiovascular effects and long-term PM2.5 exposures in multi-city models conducted in the U.S. and Europe . . . Recent studies have provided new evidence linking long-term exposure to PM2.5 with an array of cardiovascular effects such as heart attacks, congestive heart failure, stroke and mortality. <u>This evidence is coherent with studies of short-term exposure to PM2.5 that have observed associations with a continuum of effects ranging from subtle changes in indicators of cardiovascular health to serious clinical effects, such as increased hospitalizations and emergency department visits due to cardiovascular disease and cardiovascular mortality.</u> [Emphasis added]

As always for the EPA, PM2.5 was extremely deadly when it came to issuing new regulations, but virtually harmless when it came to exposing humans to astonishingly high doses of it.

The University of Washington had also performed human experiments on behalf of the EPA. But it was far more forthcoming with documents related to its experiments. The University of Washington's researchers also did not inform their human guinea pigs of the EPA-determined dangers of PM2.5. The consent form I received stated:[123]

Diesel exhaust is a mixture of gases and particles. The particle component of diesel exhaust consists mostly of carbon particles, commonly known as soot. These particles are often coated with toxic chemicals. Studies have shown that long-term exposure to diesel exhaust particles can cause cancer in laboratory animals. There is potential that [diesel exhaust particles] can cause cancer in humans . . . Since these effects are probably associated with long-term high-level exposures, the cancer risk from this exposure is extremely small. However, you should read and understand the additional fact sheet and have all your questions answered before signing this form.

> *Long-term diesel exposure can cause non-cancer effects. Studies with workers exposed to diesel exhaust have shown increased incidence of cough, phlegm and chronic bronchitis and reductions in pulmonary function.*
>
> *Your exposure to diesel exhaust will be for 2 hours during each of two visits (4 hours total). With short-term exposure to diesel exhaust as experienced in this study, you may experience an unpleasant odor, irritation of the eyes, nose, or bronchial irritation. Other symptoms may include nausea, lightheadedness, cough difficulty breathing, chest tightness, wheezing and phlegm production.*

This was pretty standard non-disclosure language. But within the documents was a letter from the University of Washington that further undermined the EPA's claims that the experiments were not harmful.

In October 2012, the University of Washington wrote to study subjects as follows:[124]

> *We are contacting you because at one time you participated in a study that assessed how diesel exhaust exposures affect blood vessels. Recently, a decision was made by the World Health Organization's International Agency for Research on Cancer (IARC) to reclassify diesel engine exhaust as 'carcinogenic to humans' from its previous classification of 'probably carcinogenic' to humans. The UW Human Subjects Division has asked that subjects who participated in earlier studies of diesel exhaust exposure, even though their involvement may be complete, be contacted by letter and made aware of the reclassification.*
>
> *We will continue our studies on the cardiovascular health effects of diesel exhaust as the ethical review committee has determined that the risks posed by the study are reasonable. Enclosed please find a fact sheet similar to the one you reviewed*

at the time of your study participation. The fact sheet has been updated to reflect the change in IARC classification. It is not necessary to respond to this letter but should you have any questions or require additional information, please contact us using the information provided above.

Sincerely,

Joel Kaufman, MD, MPH

In other words, "we exposed you to something that is known to cause cancer, but don't worry about it."

Working through the non-profit Committee for a Constructive Tomorrow (CFACT), I also filed a complaint with the state of Michigan's medical board requesting an investigation into the University of Michigan's Dr. Robert D. Brook. As an associate professor in the university's Department of Internal Medicine and a Michigan-licensed physician, Brook was also the principal investigator for EPA-funded human experiments with PM2.5. Brook's experiment involved exposing 50 human study subjects, ages 18 to 50 years who were obese or had metabolic syndrome, to more than 100 millionths-of-a-gram of PM2.5 per cubic meter—more than three times the EPA outdoor standard for PM2.5.

In addition to the usual litany of EPA statements about the near-instant lethality of PM2.5, I included this statement from the American Heart Association's update of its scientific statement on PM2.5:[125]

Exposure to [PM2.5] over a few hours to a few weeks can trigger cardiovascular disease-related mortality and non-fatal events . . .
Time series studies estimate that a [10 millionths-of-a-gram per cubic meter] increase in mean 24-hour PM2.5 concentration increases the relative risk for daily cardiovascular mortality by approximately 0.4 percent to 1.0 percent. Despite theoretical

*statistical risks ascribed to all individuals, this elevated risk
from exposure is not equally distributed within a population.
At present-day levels, PM2.5 likely poses an acute threat prin-
cipally to susceptible people, even if seemingly healthy, such as
the elderly and those with (unrecognized) existing coronary
artery or structural heart disease . . . Short-term increases in
PM2.5 levels lead to the early mortality of tens of thousands of
individuals per year in the United States alone.*

The lead author of that quote so condemning PM2.5 as lethal
even in "seemingly healthy" people was none other than the University
of Michigan's Dr. Robert Brook. But that was not all. In the media
release for the American Heart Association's document, Brook stated:[126]

There is no 'safe' level of PM2.5 exposure.

Yet the consent forms Brook gave to his human study subjects
described PM2.5 as entirely harmless:[127]

*There have been no reported adverse events to healthy partic-
ipants receiving similar air pollution exposures during the past
decade from research centers around the world. The air pollution you will be exposed to is concentrated from the natural
(ambient) environment and is made up of typical city air
pollution that you would breathe if you were walking down
a busy street in a large city. The concentration levels of air
pollution that you will be exposed occur in the real world
during bad air pollution days in cities or in industrial envi-
ronments. They are considered high natural (ambient) levels.
In previous studies performed by us, subjects could not tell the
difference between conditions when they breathed clean/filtered
air or the polluted air. This concentration of air pollution is
significantly less than what is found in a smoky room or bar.*

News of the University of Michigan complaint was broken by *Detroit News* columnist Henry Payne, who had the opportunity to interview Brook. As Payne reported:[128]

> *In an interview, Brook says that the tests he has conducted were board-reviewed and exposed humans subjects to unharm-ful, low levels of particulate matter less than what 'you would receive from 1 or 2 puffs on a cigarette.'*
>
> *But Brooks argument that there are levels of risk to PM2.5 exposure contradicts EPA's claims that there is no safe level of exposure.*

Brook then told Payne that he would not do anymore PM2.5 human experiments because, he implied, they were too dangerous:

> *Brook says that—while he has received EPA approval to conduct more testing—he is not going to conduct further ex-periments, though he says it has nothing to do with Milloy's complaint. 'I am not going to do these (these tests) because I don't believe in exposing people,' says Brook. 'I have shown PM2.5 is bad for you.'*

A week later, in response to Payne's column, a letter to the editor from Dr. Marc Peters-Golden, a professor at the University of Michigan Medical School and a colleague of Brook's, was published:[129]

> *Henry Payne's July 23rd column on the EPA's tests on the health effects of particulate pollution seeks to alarm the public, but merely confuses . . .*
>
> *It parrots views long espoused by Steve Milloy, a consultant with a long history of fighting for tobacco and oil companies and against common-sense public health measures. I would like to clarify why scientists consider the type of research crit-*

icized by Payne to be so essential and to put to rest his concerns about its danger.

A very large body of research conducted around the world has shown that fine particulate pollution is associated with a number of serious health problems, most notably conditions affecting the respiratory and cardiovascular systems. There is little debate among scientists about these risks, but what is not well understood is how particles lead to these outcomes. By measuring short-term changes in biological markers in exposed subjects, research such as that conducted by Dr. Brook helps scientists understand the sequence of bodily events that can, in the long term, lead to adverse health effects. This type of information can only be obtained in controlled research settings where other variables, such as weather conditions and other pollutants, are eliminated.

Importantly, this valuable information can be obtained without jeopardizing subjects' health, since the level of particulate matter administered in these experiments is no greater than what would be inhaled on a smoggy day in any number of big cities. An underlying tenet of such research is that it must be reviewed and approved by Institutional Review Boards charged with ensuring the safety of subjects.

Research such as this is vital for helping guide public health policy. Columns such as Payne's are a disservice not only to the truth but also to the public's well being.

Although Brook himself renounced the experiments to Payne, Brook's colleague defended them. Also despite his renunciation, Brook won the battle at the Michigan medical board in October 2013. The medical board denied my request to investigate, as usual, without explanation.[130]

Soon enough, though, official vindication of my charges would come from the most unexpected place of all—the EPA's own inspector general.

CHAPTER 22

A Surprise from the EPA Inspector General

The EPA Inspector General's report was quite the indictment of the EPA's PM2.5 human experiments.

First, the Inspector General noted that EPA did in fact state that PM2.5 killed people:[131]

> *In a 2003 fact sheet, the EPA's message to the public about PM2.5 was that long-term exposure is associated with reduced lung function and even premature death and short-term exposure is linked to heart attacks and arrhythmias for people with heart disease. A 2006 EPA assessment document further reports associations between short-term PM exposures and mortality and morbidity.*

Keeping in mind that the inspector general report was limited to only the 81 study subjects in the KINGCON, OMEGACON and XCON studies—and two other studies involving diesel exhaust, called DEPOZ and LAMARCK—the inspector general continued:

> *The XCON and DEPOZ study consent forms warned the study subjects that exposure to high levels of selected air pollutants (i.e., PM, the pollutant being tested in the XCON study and diesel exhaust, the pollutant being tested in the*

151

DEPOZ study) could lead to death in older people with car-diovascular problems. This warning was not in the OMEGACON, KINGCON or LAMARCK consent forms, even though these studies also exposed study subjects to PM (OMEGACON, KINGCON) and diesel exhaust (LAMARCK). According to an NHEERL manager, the exposure risk for healthy individuals is minimal. Because the three studies' consent forms (OMEGACON, KINGCON and LAMARCK) lacked the warning that PM exposure can cause death in older people with cardiovascular disease, they are significantly different in their disclosure of exposure risk than the XCON and DEPOZ consent forms. This lack of warning about PM in OMEGACON, KINGCON and LAMARCK is also different from the EPA's public message about PM. [Emphasis added]

So there it was in that last sentence. EPA was telling the public and the study subjects different stories.

The inspector general also cited EPA for failing to warn study subjects about the cancer risk from the diesel exhaust experiments, as follows:

The LAMARCK and DEPOZ study consent forms did not include the potential cancer effects of long-term exposure to diesel exhaust. The EPA classifies diesel exhaust as 'likely to be carcinogenic to humans by inhalation' and stated in its 2002 Health Assessment Document for Diesel Engine Exhaust that long-term inhalation exposure is likely to pose a lung cancer hazard to humans, as well as damage the lung in other ways depending on the length of the exposure. According to EPA's 2002 Health Assessment document, the human evidence from occupational studies is considered strongly supportive of a finding that diesel exhaust exposure is causally associated with lung cancer, though the evidence is less than that needed to definitively conclude that diesel exhaust is carcinogenic to humans . . .

> *An August 2013 article in the* Journal of Clinical Best Practices *states that 'most people would want to know whether a medical procedure involves a risk of death, even if the chance of dying is very small.' One study subject that we interviewed stated that it would have been useful to have had information about known long-term effects of exposure to diesel exhaust. In our view, the EPA should inform study subjects of the potential long-term cancer risk of any pollutant to which it exposes human subjects so that study subjects can make the most informed decision possible about whether to participate in a study.* [Emphasis added]

The inspector general reached the following conclusion:

> *The EPA obtained informed consent from the 81 study subjects that participated in the five studies in 2010 and 2011 as required by [the Common Rule]. However, the EPA inconsistently addressed pollutant risk in its consent forms. Only two of the five studies' consent forms included the risk of death from exposure to high levels of selected air pollutants such as PM and diesel exhaust and only one study's consent form included the upper limits of exposure levels. Because EPA's regulations do not define 'reasonably foreseeable risks,' EPA investigators, the [Institutional Review Board] and the human studies research review official must define the term using their professional judgment, which leads to inconsistencies in addressing risks in the study consent forms. Such inconsistencies could lead to inconsistent protection of human subjects. The EPA needs to develop guidance to help ensure more consistent interpretation of reasonably foreseeable risks. Furthermore, the EPA should provide the study subjects with a summary of the EPA assessments about the short- and long-term effects of the pollutants to which human study subjects will be exposed.*

> *The EPA's diesel exhaust studies did not include language*
> *about the long-term cancer risks of diesel exhaust. The NHEERL*
> *manager explained that the cancer risk from diesel exhaust*
> *was not relevant to the 2-hour exposures included in the*
> *LAMARCK study. However, evidence suggests that at least*
> *some human study subjects would like to know if a study*
> *involves risk of death, even if the risk is very small. In the*
> *future, the EPA should include the long-term risk of cancer*
> *to potential subjects in its consent forms so study subjects can*
> *make the most informed decision about whether to partici-*
> *pate in a study.*

The report also had another upside—this part of the EPA PM2.5 human experimentation scandal finally made a major media breakthrough. Though the issue had previously been covered by some conservative media and also on an ongoing basis by an NBC-TV affiliate in North Carolina, on April 2, 2014 it made the very top of the Drudge Report with the headline:

SHOCK REPORT: EPA tested deadly pollutants
on human beings.

The next day the *Drudge Report* added the headline:

Experiments on children?

The Associated Press ran the headline, "EPA Fails to Disclose Risks in Human Tests."[132] The New York Times headline was "EPA Faulted for Failure to Report Risks" and the Washington Post followed with "EPA did not disclose cancer risks in tests." [133, 134]

After the issuance of the Inspector General report, I was contacted by staff of the House Space, Science and Technology Committee about possibly having a hearing on the report. But the prospect for a hearing fizzled when the EPA told the Committee that it would not cooperate and would refuse to appear at such a hearing. When the EPA can tell a Congressional committee with oversight authority over the agency in effect to "get lost," you can understand how the EPA can get away with its rogue conduct.

One might think that the Inspector General report and the negative major media publicity it generated would have chastened the EPA somewhat. But that would be wrong.

In mid-June 2016, a source in the government telephoned and told me that he had inadvertently stumbled upon a review of the EPA human testing program being conducted by a committee of the prestigious National Academy of Sciences (NAS). He gave me the link to the NAS committee's web site and, sure enough, the committee was reviewing EPA's human experimentation program in response to the March 2014 EPA Inspector General report.

The web site indicated that the NAS committee held a meeting open to the public on June 1, 2015 and then had met four times privately since, with the last meeting being held in April 2016. I immediately telephoned the NAS staff person managing the committee to learn that the committee had finished its all its planned meetings and was in the process of writing its final report. He directed me to the public docket for the committee for what information had already been presented to the committee at the lone public meeting.

The public docket revealed that the committee had only been presented with information supplied by the EPA. The agenda for the committee's public hearing revealed that only committee members and EPA staff were in attendance. This was not so surprising when I searched but could find no public notice of the committee's formation or the "public meeting." When queried, NAS staff could only point to the committee's web page as any sort of "public notice." But then again, there was no public notice that the committee had been formed, so how would anyone in the public know to look for its web site?

I hurriedly put together and submitted comments for the public docket and asked NAS staff for an in-person opportunity to present my side of the EPA human testing story to the committee. I made the same request to the individual committee members. Weeks passed with no response.

Tired of waiting, toward the end of July I published a commentary on the situation in the *Washington Times*. I accused the EPA of covertly hiring the NAS to rehabilitate the EPA's illegal human experiments. The commentary concluded with the following:[135]

> *Now I have dealt with the EPA for over 25 years. As detailed on this page many times, I have come not to expect good faith or honesty from the agency. The NAS on the other hand is a different matter.*
>
> *The NAS holds itself out as "nation's pre-eminent source of high-quality, objective advice on science, engineering, and health matters." If that is true, the NAS is certainly doing itself and its elite membership no favors by being paid to conduct a secret and ill-informed whitewashing of EPA's illegal conduct.*

This seems to have done the trick. Not too long after commentary ran, I was contacted and informed that I and two of my colleagues—emergency room physician Dr. John Dunn and statistician Dr. Stan Young—would each be given 30-minute slots at a newly scheduled public meeting of the committee.

My August 24, 2016 presentation reached two main conclusions. First, based on the EPA-determined lethality of PM2.5, the EPA-determined "vulnerable" nature of the study subjects, the failure to obtain proper informed consent and other reasons, the EPA's PM2.5 human experiments were fundamentally unethical, if not entirely illegal. Second, the EPA had improperly withheld key information from Institutional Review Boards, study subjects and even the NAS committee itself.

The implication of these conclusions was that, if PM2.5 was as dangerous as the EPA claimed, then its experiments violated every law and regulation established for the protection of human study subjects since the Nuremberg Code. The only way the EPA didn't have this sort of legal culpability, was if PM2.5 was not as dangerous as the EPA has told the public and Congress. There is no third option or explanation available to the EPA.

The NAS committee listened in stony silence to the presentations. Only one committee member asked any questions during the meeting. Either committee members needed more time to review the new information presented or they couldn't wait for the meeting to end so the committee could get on with the rehabilitation on behalf of the EPA. As of press time for this book, the NAS committee had not issued its report.

CHAPTER 23

Hiding the Data

Criticizing the EPA's epidemiologic studies on PM2.5 had always been an exercise in futility. This was not because the EPA's epidemiology was any good or that such criticism was difficult. Instead, the problem was that there was no way to compel the EPA to debate the issue in a bona fide and public manner. The EPA is expert at turning perfectly valid, clear-cut criticism of its analyses into *Alice in Wonderland*-like debates that no one has the time, patience or interest in listening to.

First, there is the nature of epidemiology itself. Contrary to popular perception, epidemiology is not any sort of science; it is merely applied statistics. It took, of course, the lawsuit against the EPA's human experiments to get the agency to admit this. Recall the EPA explained how epidemiology related to PM2.5 as follows:

> *Epidemiological studies do not generally provide direct evidence of causation; instead they <u>indicate the existence or absence of a statistical relationship</u>. Large population studies cannot assess the biological mechanisms that could explain how inhaling ambient air pollution particles can cause illness or death in susceptible individuals.* [Emphasis added]

The human experiments were supposed to provide the scientific piece of the puzzle—that PM2.5 could actually kill people.

Despite the purely statistical nature of epidemiology, the EPA generally presents its statistics as science. In an April 2014 speech at the National Academy of Sciences in Washington, D.C., defending EPA against critics, EPA Administrator Gina McCarthy stated, in relevant part:[136]

> *Through science, we've set health-based air quality standards that protect those most vulnerable—our children, our elderly and our infirm . . . we use the science on mercury, acid rain, ozone pollution, particulate matter and more.*

But the EPA began regulating PM2.5 before there was any science showing that it caused harm. And since the EPA's PM2.5 experiments had not killed or harmed anyone, there was, in fact, no science to back up the EPA's claim that PM2.5 kills—only dubious statistical studies. But it took a lawsuit to get the EPA to make this concession.

So now consider how difficult it is to argue statistics with EPA when it won't even admit that its statistical studies are just that. To the media and public, the EPA just brazenly declares its statistics to be "science."

It is, in fact, impossible to debate statistics with EPA as the raising of specific technical deficiencies and even outright statistical malpractice—if the EPA deigns to respond to them at all—are responded to with confusing gobbledygook that is incomprehensible to the public and politicians. It is difficult to grab and maintain the attention of people who don't have the patience or expertise to comprehend numerical arcana.

The other big problem is that there is simply no way to compel the EPA to address scientific (or statistical criticism). As demonstrated by our lawsuit and as any environmental lawyer can tell you, it is very difficult (and expensive) to get the EPA in court. If a lawyer is fortunate enough to force the EPA to defend itself in court, the law usually prevents any judicial review of factual issues relating to the science and statistics used as the basis for in any particular regulation.

A major barrier to challenging EPA science in court is the 1984 Supreme Court case, Chevron USA v. Natural Resources Defense Council.[137] In Chevron, the Court ruled that federal agencies have a great deal of discretion in interpreting the laws they administer. Since Congress does not typically instruct the EPA in how to do science, when it comes to science, the agency does virtually what it pleases. The only limitation on the EPA's authority under Chevron is that the agency's interpretation must be "reasonable." Pretty much the only way EPA can abuse its Chevron discretion is to fail to provide a rationale for what it wants to do. The rationale doesn't actually have to make sense, it just has to be stated.

The classic scenario is an EPA rulemaking procedure. After the EPA publishes a proposed rule in the Federal Register, the public is offered the opportunity to comment, including on any science used to formulate the rule. To satisfy its Chevron requirement, the EPA typically responds to what it perceives are substantive comments from people who might be able or likely to file lawsuits against the rule. These responses typically start out with something akin to, "The EPA disagrees with this view." This is then followed by whatever explanation the EPA feels like making, the mere existence of which satisfies the Chevron requirement of being reasonable. It also pretty much terminates anyone's right to further dispute the issue with the EPA in court.

It is also important to note the media's role in permitting the EPA to escape scrutiny. If the media covers criticism of EPA, it is only reluctantly and because the story is so big they cannot avoid reporting on it such as the allegations about EPA's illegal human experiments. One major reason for this reluctance is that media access to the EPA sources depends on remaining in the EPA's good graces.

Another major reason is politics. The EPA is a politicized agency and so its political allies in the media tend only to write hagiographic stories about the agency. Finally, most reporters who cover environment issues tend to be young, inexperienced and uneducated on environmental issues, science and economics. In combination with the need for access and the politics of their news organization, their reporting tends toward being more akin to public relations work for the EPA.

So having watched the EPA avoid any meaningful challenge of the science underlying its PM2.5 rules, the question became what was something that the EPA seemed to be worried about? That was easy to answer—secret science.

In 1997, the EPA had defied a Congressional request by refusing to provide the scientific data underlying the all-important Harvard Six Cities and Pope studies on PM2.5 described earlier. In 2003, the Supreme Court had rejected a challenge to the 1998 law requiring that scientific data used to support regulatory actions be made available to the public via the Freedom of Information Act. The Court said the law did not provide for judicial review and, therefore, no one could sue to enforce it.

In March 2011, I raised the secret science issue with staff of the House Space, Science and Technology Committee, who soon thereafter revived it with the EPA. At a hearing in September 2011, Rep. Andy Harris (R-Md.), a physician and chairman of the Committee's Subcommittee on Energy and the Environment, quizzed Gina McCarthy, then assistant administrator for EPA's Office of Air and Radiation, about PM2.5 and asked for the Harvard Six Cities and Pope study data:[138]

Chairman [Ralph] Hall. The Chair now recognizes the gentleman from Maryland, Mr. Harris, for three minutes.

Mr. Harris. Thank you very much, Mr. Chairman and thank you, Ms. McCarthy, for appearing before the Committee.

I have a question. As a physician, I just am curious that the claim that this somehow saves money says that we avoid up to 34,000 premature deaths. Could you break that down to what these premature deaths are due to?

Ms. McCarthy. I can tell you that the analysis we do is on the basis of health data. It looks at exposure—

Mr. Harris. I understand. Can you just break that down? What are these deaths due to?

Chairman Hall. He is not asking you what your practice is. What did you do in this—

Ms. McCarthy. The deaths are due to the pollution—

Mr. Harris. No, no, no. What diseases? You can use specific diagnoses for me. I will understand them.

Ms. McCarthy. Well, I wouldn't want to presume that I could articulate them to the extent that you could understand them. We would have respiratory illnesses, heart illnesses—

Mr. Harris. Well, you say 15,000 heart attacks per year. If every one of those patients died, I could see that is 15,000. The estimated number of asthma deaths per year on the EPA website is 10,000 per year due to exacerbations, so that would be 25,000 if every one of those was attributed to this. How do you get up to 34,000? I mean and I am used to science. When they say up to 34,000, there is usually a confidence interval there. You know, it is like one to 34,000 or 10 to 34,000. Why would you use something so unscientific to say up to 34,000?

Ms. McCarthy. The health data is all part of the record and I would indicate to you that we are looking at health benefits—

Mr. Harris. Okay. Thank you. And I would appreciate—

Ms. McCarthy [continuing]. Across the United States.

Mr. Harris. Sure, I understand that and if you could get me that information, I would appreciate it. Now, is that health data due to the particulates or the ozone?

Ms. McCarthy. It would mostly be the particulate matter but—

Mr. Harris. Weren't these numbers the same numbers, though, that were floated around a week ago when the administration suspended its ozone standards?

Ms. McCarthy. Clearly not, no.

Mr. Harris. They weren't?

Ms. McCarthy. No, they were not.

Mr. Harris. What were those figures?

Ms. McCarthy. I actually don't have them at the top of my head but I certainly can provide them.

Mr. Harris. I would appreciate that, because I recall that the deaths in the press reports from the advocates were very, very similar to that and there is evidence, I think, that 90 percent of the health benefit claimed by the EPA under this rule are for particulates, so I am just curious about that, how many times you can count a death for a rule for its proposed benefit.

Ms. McCarthy. We do that—

Mr. Harris. Are those particulate matter, the data that supports that death and injury data, is that publicly available?

Ms. McCarthy. Yes.

Mr. Harris. Could you get that to me?

Ms. McCarthy. Yes, sir.

Mr. Harris. Thank you very much, because I would love to have it, you know, reviewed independently from the EPA.

Ms. McCarthy. I think I should probably clarify only because I just realized what you are indicating is that the 15,000 heart attacks that we reference are nonfatal, so that would be very different than thinking that we—

Mr. Harris. That is even worse because the number of people that have a heart attack who go on to die actually now under current therapy is actually quite low, so the numbers of deaths from heart attacks actually would be strikingly low as part of that 34,000, so I am just curious about that.

But anyway, my time is expired. Thank you, Mr. Chairman and I appreciate follow-up on those two questions I asked. Thank you.

As McCarthy was incorrect about the "death and injury data" being publicly available, Congressman Harris made his request clear in a follow-up letter that read:[139]

I questioned you about the availability of the data that support the death and injury benefits and you assured me that all such data is publicly available and you were willing to provide it. In light of the pivotal role of this publicly-funded research in providing a justification for major EPA regulations, it is imperative that associated data and analysis be open and transparent to allow for sufficient scientific and technical review. Accordingly, in the spirit and letter of Public Law 105-277, Executive Order 13563 (which explicitly states that regulations "must be based on the best available science," EPA's Peer Review Handbook and recently—released Scientific Integrity Policy Draft, please provide all original data and analysis for the following rules that were used in the EPA analysis:

    1. The Cancer Prevention Study I compiled by the American Cancer Society.

    2. The Cancer Prevention Study II compiled by the American Cancer Society.

    3. The Harvard Six Cities Study.

    4. The Nurses' Health Study and Nurses Health Study II.

Please provide all this information no later than October 3, 2011.

But the deadline came and went and Congressman Harris had received no data from the EPA. Nor would any be forthcoming. The EPA once again ignored a specific request from Congress—and likely not without good reason. The requested health data would likely be really embarrassing for the EPA if anyone other than an EPA-friendly researcher obtained it. So while House Science Committee staff continued pursuing the EPA on the secret science issue, I went back to the drawing board for an entirely new approach to the PM2.5 problem.

CHAPTER 24

Overcoming EPA's Secret Science

Since mere criticism of the EPA's science had virtually no chance of success and no meaningful political or media pressure was forthcoming, a new plan to expose the EPA junk science was required. Although the EPA's PM2.5 claims had so far proven to be unsupportable, if not outright false, short of a smoking gun email between EPA staff admitting that PM2.5 was a huge scientific fraud, persuasive evidence against the EPA would have to be created. That meant someone had to do some sort of new study of PM2.5 and mortality.

To prove the EPA wrong via a new study seemed impossible. Where would anyone get the data to show that PM2.5 doesn't kill anyone? The EPA certainly wouldn't provide the data. Neither would the owners of the data underlying the Harvard Six Cities and Pope studies. Friendly statisticians I talked to were stumped as well. So new data would need to be created. But how and what kind of data would it have to be?

If the EPA's claim was that PM2.5 killed on a same-day-as-inhalation basis, then data on daily PM2.5 measurements and daily deaths would be required. Daily PM2.5 measurements for pretty much any geographic area were relatively easy to come by since the EPA and many states make their daily air quality data available on their web sites. But daily death data would be harder to find, if it could be found at all. Even the EPA didn't actually rely on death data collected

167

on a daily basis. Its researchers typically relied on death data collected on an annual basis.

The federal government and states do make death statistics available to the public, but these tend to be summary statistics that are maintained and presented on an annual basis. These summaries let you know how many people died in any given year, but not how many people died on each day. So even the EPA's own researchers did not have much daily death data.

It occurred to me that hospitals might be a good source of daily data since they must keep records of who is admitted for what and what the outcome was. It also occurred to me that I might be able use the Freedom of Information Act to obtain daily data from federal hospitals, such those operated by the Veterans Administration. But that idea began to fade as I realized that hospital death data would be useless since they only represent a too small and non-representative subset of deaths in a particular geographic region.

But the idea of gleaning information from a hospital was a start. So I decided to change health endpoints for the sake of testing the Freedom of Information Act as a tool for creating new data. Other than death, the EPA's other adverse health effect that it liked to blame on outdoor air quality was asthma. The agency was fond of claiming that by reducing outdoor levels of PM2.5 and ground-level smog or ozone, hospital emergency room visits for asthma would be reduced.

As Los Angeles had been used by the EPA in the human experiments as an example of a "smoggy city," I fired off a Freedom of Information Act request to the Veterans Administration (VA) West Los Angeles Medical Center. To my utter amazement it worked. Within weeks, I received from the hospital a day-by-day tally of emergency room admissions for asthma for the period between January 1, 2009, through December 31, 2011. I put the asthma data in a spreadsheet along with daily ozone measurements made by the state of California and computed the statistical correlations.

Based on the 726 emergency room visits for asthma at the VA

West Los Angeles Medical Center during the period 2009 to 2011, my data showed that there was no correlation between ozone levels and asthma admissions. I published this result on JunkScience.com with the note:[140]

The study data are available upon request.

Now while it's certainly true that this VA Medical Center analysis was just statistical in nature and not scientific—just like the EPA's epidemiologic studies—the statistics were nonetheless valuable as an exploratory tool.

Back in the day before epidemiology was corrupted by political agendas like the EPA's, any epidemiologist worth his salt would first run the sort of quick-and-dirty correlational analysis that was done here. The purpose of such an analysis is to quickly and easily check to see if the data might reveal any correlations worthy of interest and further analysis. If there are no potential correlations of interest, an old-school epidemiologist would typically just move on to greener research pastures.

The data obtained from the Los Angeles VA Medical Center offered no indication that air quality was in any way associated with hospital admissions for asthma, so case closed.

But while the air in the Los Angeles area can be some of the "worst" air in the U.S., the air in west Los Angeles tends not to be a problem because of its proximity to the coast. The breeze clears the air. So I knew I had to find some place known for "bad air" and that also had a hospital accessible via the Freedom of Information Act. A request was sent for asthma admissions data from the entire University of California-Davis health system under California's Public Records Act. Once again, amazingly enough, the raw data came easily.

I put all the data in a spreadsheet—19,327 hospital admissions for asthma for the three-year period from January 1, 2010 to December 31, 2012—and reported no correlation between ozone or PM2.5 and asthma admissions. Based on this large analysis I concluded:[141]

> *If ambient ozone and PM2.5 measurements were in fact asso-*
> *ciated with hospital admissions for asthma, one could reasonably*
> *expect—and, in fact—ought to find some correlation in these*
> *data. But such a correlation was not identified.*

Though I didn't waste time with publishing this analysis in a mainstream journal, I noted at the end of my write-up:

> *The study data are available upon request.*

Of course, anyone could get this data since it was all accessible through federal and state right-to-know laws.

I finally hit the jackpot, though, shortly after publication of the VA West Los Angeles Medical Center data. Surfing the vital statistics pages of the state of California's Health and Human Services Agency in search of more data, I ran across something called "Death Public Use Files." Clicking on the link, I was astounded to find that every death certificate in the state of California from 1998 onward could be obtained in electronic format.

While each death certificate was stripped of personal identifying information, like name and address, what remained was the key data of use to researchers: date of birth, date of death, age, cause of death and zip code. For a cost of $100 per year, this data could be purchased for research-only purposes. So I bought it all and, without too much hassle, within four months, I was the proud owner of 1.8 million official death certificates from the state of California covering the period 1998 through 2010.

I eagerly dove into the massive data dump. The most difficult challenge in utilizing the data was how to associate death certificates, which could be sorted by zip code, with PM2.5 data, which was maintained by the state of California on the basis of the state's "air basin" system.

California regulators have divided the state into 15 air basins, which are geographic regions with similar meteorological and air quality conditions, like the San Francisco Bay region and the South Coast region, which includes Los Angeles. But there are over 2,600 zip codes in California, some of which overlap air basins. Assigning death certificates to air basins seemed like it would take forever to do. Fortunately, a very nice woman at the California Air Resources Board was able to provide a key that mapped zip codes into air basins. With that help, it took about a month of half-time work to complete the analysis, but the effort was most rewarding.

CHAPTER 25

Unlocking the Truth

The California study unlocked the truth about the EPA's statistical fairytale.

The EPA's claim that any amount of PM2.5 can cause death within hours would finally be tested by comparing daily PM2.5 measurements from across the state of California with the daily number of deaths across the state. The goal was to see whether PM2.5 levels were at all correlated with the number of deaths. If so, then as PM2.5 levels increased, the number of deaths should also increase either the same day, next day or day-after-next day. If a sufficiently large and statistically significant correlation were identified, that would lend some credence to EPA's claims.

Once again, this would not be science, only a statistical analysis. But if this analysis could not produce a meaningful statistical correlation between daily PM2.5 measurements and daily death counts, then that alone would pretty much torpedo the EPA's claims.

The analysis covered the four-year period from January 1, 2007 through December 31, 2010. The reason for selecting this time frame was that the state of California didn't have complete PM2.5 monitoring data across all major air basins until 2007 and the most recent death certificate data available at the time I made my request went through 2010. But four years of data is certainly sufficient for testing EPA's notion that PM2.5 kills on a same-day, next-day or day-after-the-next basis.

The analysis included 854,109 deaths, which represented about 94 percent of the deaths that occurred in California during that time frame. These 854,109 deaths occurred in eight of 15 California air basins. The seven air basins that were omitted were omitted because the air is so pristine that the state of California doesn't even bother to monitor PM2.5 levels on a daily basis. They are also areas with small populations.

The number of deaths also represented (at that time) by far the largest epidemiologic study on PM2.5 of its kind—that is, comparing PM2.5 with deaths on a daily basis. For perspective on this point, the largest PM2.5 study ever published involved 2.2 million deaths from across the country during the period 2000 through 2006 (the "Greven study").[142] But in the Greven study the PM2.5-versus-deaths comparison was performed only on a monthly basis. Such a study could obviously not test EPA's claim that PM2.5 kills on a daily basis.

The daily analysis I did, in fact, had never been performed on such as large-scale before.

Another strength of the California study over the other studies is that it covered virtually the entire state of California. Cities and counties to study were not cherry-picked. The only areas that were excluded were those that were not monitored because the air was clean and had relatively small populations. The Greven study, in contrast, selected study subjects because they lived within six miles of one of only 518 PM2.5 monitors in the eastern half of the U.S. As EPA operates about 5,000 monitors across the country, selecting 518 of them is far from comprehensive.

So what were the results of the California study?

The data showed absolutely no meaningful correlation between daily PM2.5 measurements and daily deaths across the state of California or in any air basin.[143] This was also true when the deaths occurred on a same day, next day and day-after next day basis. Even when I looked at deaths by category—like deaths from all causes, deaths from non-violent causes, deaths from heart disease, deaths from lung disease, deaths from heart and lung disease combined and deaths in the aforesaid categories for people 65 years of age and older—there was no correlation between PM2.5 exposure and death. Even when I looked at short-term spikes in PM2.5 measurements lasting a few days or a week in various air basins, the numbers of daily deaths did not increase.

The data also shed light on the how EPA's researchers pulled-off their epidemiologic handiwork—they selected the data that they know would give them the result they wanted. But before we discuss those results, a short primer on statistical correlations is in order.

The range of values for correlations is negative one (-1.0) to positive one (1.0). A correlation of 1.0 between two phenomena means that the two phenomena change in perfectly in sync with each other. As one phenomenon appears, increases or decrease, so does the other in lock step. A correlation of negative one, called an "inverse correlation," means that the two phenomenon change in precisely opposite ways from one another. As one increases, the other decreases and so forth.

A correlation of precisely zero means that the two phenomena change totally independent of one another. So far, this is pretty simple. But what does it mean when a correlation lies somewhere between negative one and zero or zero and positive one. In these cases, which represent virtually all correlations ever calculated, judgment is required to interpret the potential meaning of the correlation.

For ease of discussion we will just focus on correlations between zero and positive one, though the exact same analysis can be applied for correlations between negative one and zero. Even better, you won't have to take my word for any of the following. We will rely on the EPA's own views on how to interpret correlations.[144] According to the EPA, which takes a conventional view of correlations: (1) When a correlation approaches positive one (like 0.86, which is the EPA's example), that indicates a correlation between two phenomena;

(2) When a correlation is less than midway between zero and one (like 0.37 which is the EPA's example), that indicates a "weak" association that which you shouldn't have much confidence in; and (3) When a correlation approaches zero (like 0.04, which is the EPA's example), that is essentially a zero correlation indicating no association between the two phenomena in question.

So applying the EPA's standards to the analysis of the daily California PM2.5 levels and daily deaths in California, we get some very interesting results over the 90 different correlations calculated from the California data.

The correlation between PM2.5 levels and total deaths in California was 0.03, which according to the EPA's standards, means there is no correlation between PM2.5 and deaths from all causes in California. This correlation was based on 854,109 deaths, which is a lot.

But the phenomenon of "deaths from all causes" is overly broad as, for example, deaths from violence cannot be blamed on PM2.5. So the death category was then confined to just those deaths that are heart and lung related, which is how the EPA claims PM2.5 kills. The correlation between PM2.5 levels and deaths from heart and lung causes was precisely zero, again meaning PM2.5 is not associated with death. This correlation was based on 377,199 deaths—again a lot of deaths.

But remember that the EPA claims that the elderly are among the most vulnerable to the alleged effects of PM2.5. For the 310,047 deaths in this category, the correlation between PM2.5 and deaths was precisely zero. So the analysis showed that for virtually the entire state of California during the years 2007 through 2010, PM2.5 could not be correlated with death as claimed by the EPA.

A noteworthy observation from the analysis was that each California air basin tended to have similar correlations in each category year-after-year. For example, the correlations for the San Francisco Bay air basin were always slightly positive around a positive 0.13. In contrast, the correlations in the South Coast air basin (that is, the Los Angeles area) were always slightly negative around a negative 0.08. So does this mean that PM2.5 might kill people in San Francisco, but might help them live longer in Los Angeles? Of course, not. What it means is that there is some unaccounted for underlying factor in the two areas that is not PM2.5 that caused the correlations to differ. It was still revealing, however, as it suggests a hypothesis for how the EPA's researchers slant their results.

When the EPA's researchers pick their geographic areas for studying PM2.5 and death, they are careful to compile the mix of geographic locations that will give them the net correlation result they want. It's also possible that there are other variables in the analysis that can be similarly cherry-picked or manipulated to produce EPA-desired results. It's not necessarily ingenious, but it is clever enough that no one would ever untangle their scheme—unless you did the work for yourself. It's no wonder the EPA refuses to reveal to Congress, the public and independent researchers the data used in the Harvard Six City and Pope studies.

A final insight revealed by the California study was the utter impossibility of credibly observing within the PM2.5 epidemiologic data the size of the association the EPA says exists between PM2.5 and death.

In the South Coast air basin for example, the one containing Los Angeles, on average about 122 people die every day from heart and lung causes. The 95 percent margin of error on that average is plus/minus 42 deaths from heart/lung causes. The EPA estimates that the population death rate increases 1 percent per 10 millionth-of-a-gram per cubic meter increase in PM2.5.

So if the PM2.5 in South Coast air increases by 10 millionths-of-a-gram per cubic meter, then we would expect to see the death increase from 122 per day to 123.2 per day—except how could this be observed given the daily death toll in the South Coast air basin normally ranges, regardless of PM2.5, as high as 164? To get the South Coast air basin's daily death toll out of the range of uncertainty, as per EPA claims, the daily PM2.5 level would have to shoot up by at least 420 millionths-of-a-gram per cubic meter. As the PM2.5 level in the South Coast air basin only exceeded 35 millionths-of-a-gram per cubic meter for 9 days in 2014 with a maximum reading at a single monitor of 97 millionths-of-a-gram per cubic meter, it would be practically impossible to attribute a death to PM2.5.

There are two further points to make in closing this chapter. First, the California data is already publicly available, so anyone can check the analysis if they are so inclined. Next, someone already has checked my work and released the results. A team of statisticians led by world-class air quality statistician Richard Smith of the University of North Carolina took my idea and conducted an even larger study based on the California death certificates.

Once again covering the eight California air basins with PM2.5 data, but this time for the expanded time frame of 2000 through 2012, Smith found no association between PM2.5 and premature death among the 2 million deaths included in the analysis.[145] Though Smith's analysis is far more complex than mine, we both got the same result—PM2.5 is not associated with short-term death. Smith's data is publicly available as well.

These studies are not the first epidemiologic studies to report no statistical association between PM2.5 and death. I mentioned one earlier that I offered up when challenged by the Environmental Defense Fund on my "Show Us the Bodies, EPA" commentary. There are many others as well.[146]

Perhaps the most prominent study that contradicts EPA's PM2.5 claims is an EPA-funded study involving 3.2 million deaths that occurred during 2000 and 2006 in 814 U.S. locations. Those EPA-funded researchers reported no association between PM2.5 and death within any of the 814 locations studied.[147] This obviously embarrassing result apparently compelled EPA to request that the researchers explain themselves—or more accurately, explain away their results. In memo to the EPA, the researchers tried to explain and/or apologize as follows:[148]

> *Our results do not invalidate previous epidemiological studies . . . . We did not find evidence of a local effect and we instead found evidence of a national effect. Although these results call for additional investigation of why we found these differences between the local and national effects, these results do not invalidate results of other cohort and multi-site time series studies.*

This "national effect" the study authors refer to is similar to the differences between, say, the South Coast and San Francisco air basins previously described in the California study. It is obviously not an effect due to PM2.5 but, instead, is due to some other unaccounted-for risk factor for death, or even just chance. If PM2.5 is not associated with death on a local level, it cannot be associated with death on a national level. In other words, if PM2.5 is the killer EPA describes it as, then it kills everywhere all the time—not just when the numbers are convenient for EPA.

CHAPTER 26

EPA Fails Every Test

In making its claim that PM2.5 is deadly, the EPA relies on three lines of evidence: the epidemiological studies, animal toxicology studies and human experiments. Yet none of these lines of evidence supports the EPA's claims. Moreover, a fourth line of evidence, the real world, utterly debunks them.

Thanks to the human experiments lawsuit, the EPA has already admitted that the epidemiology by itself does not prove that PM2.5 causes death. As EPA stated in its initial response to our complaint:

> *However epidemiological studies do not generally provide direct evidence of causation; instead <u>they indicate the existence or absence of a statistical relationship</u>. Large population studies cannot assess the biological mechanisms that could explain how inhaling ambient air pollution particles can cause illness or death in susceptible individuals.* [Emphasis added]

From a purely scientific viewpoint, there is no need to discuss the PM2.5 epidemiology any further. It is just statistics and unless there is some biological or medical evidence that supports the statistics, such as would be developed from the human experiments or animal toxicology tests, the epidemiology results remain as mere statistics. And mere statistics are not science and certainly not sufficient evidence for determining a causal relationship between breathing PM2.5 and death. Nevertheless, the PM2.5 epidemiology is worth some additional examination to understand just how utterly inadequate it is as evidence that PM2.5 kills.

Epidemiology, or more plainly just "statistics," can be a very valuable public health tool. But it is like any other tool; it must be used for the right purpose. You wouldn't, for example, use a telescope to study DNA. Epidemiology's usefulness is limited to observing a relatively high rate of a relatively rare disease in a population. As previously discussed, epidemiology is a useful tool is in the analysis of, say, a food poisoning incident in which there is a sudden outbreak of intestinal illness.

After gathering data about the victims—what and where they ate—statistical analysis can then be used to identify potential culprits, like a specific food supplied by a particular vendor. Then laboratory science can take over to see which culprit actually harbored the suspected infectious agent. The data relied upon in a mass food poisoning case is typically gathered while the incident is ongoing or in its immediate aftermath and is usually pretty reliable. If I'm sick today, I'll know what and where I ate yesterday. This temporal proximity of exposure-illness-investigation gives this sort of epidemiologic investigation a high probability of success.

This stands in stark contrast to the EPA's PM2.5 epidemiology, which violates the basic requirement of studying a high rate of a relative rare disease. Death is a not a rare health outcome. Everyone dies. Half the population will die before they reach life expectancy. The elderly and very sick, the populations EPA claims are most vulnerable to PM2.5, are at highest risk of dying regardless of PM2.5. There is also no medical means of determining that someone died from inhaling PM2.5 and no actual death has ever been attributed to PM2.5.

Moreover everyone is unavoidably exposed to PM2.5 given that it occurs naturally from such sources as plants (pollen), dust, molds, forest fires and volcanoes. The problem with the exposure issue is compounded by the fact that exposures used in EPA's epidemiology are mere guesswork.

A study subject's inhalation of PM2.5 is typically assumed to be whatever the air pollution monitor closest to his residence reads— even though it more than likely has no relationship to the amount of PM2.5 actually inhaled. For example, about 20 percent of the population smokes cigarettes and smoking a single cigarette might expose the smoker to up to 40,000 millionths-of-a-gram of PM2.5 in about five minutes. In contrast, a full day of breathing the "worst" U.S. air would only expose someone to a total of about 250 millionths-of-a-gram of PM2.5.

Merely walking through a cloud of secondhand smoke will dramatically increase your exposure to PM2.5 as will many dust- or smoke- and engine exhaust-related occupations, home exposures to pet dander and dust and fire-related activities like barbequing and enjoying a home fireplace. So the PM2.5 exposure "data" used in epidemiology studies is pure make-believe.

The bottom line is: If you don't know what someone was exposed to and you don't know what he or she died of, you have no basis in fact for blaming PM2.5.

As we saw in the discussion of the EPA human experiments, the EPA's non-sequitur response to these facts is that, while the epidemiology may show only a small risk of death from PM2.5 to any individual, when that risk is applied across the 300 million people in the U.S., the result is about 570,000 deaths per year. This argument is bogus because it jumps ahead of the fact that the epidemiology cannot and does not causally link PM2.5 with death. The further bad news for the EPA's rejoinder is that no other body of science or evidence supports the agency either.

Past the epidemiology, the next body of evidence the EPA attempts to rely on is the animal toxicology—research in which laboratory animals like mice, dogs and primates are exposed to extraordinarily high doses of PM2.5 in an effort to kill them. The problem for the EPA is that no animal used in these experiments has ever died from being exposed to PM2.5. But this reality has been a tough pill for the EPA to swallow.

In its 2012 PM2.5 rulemaking, EPA claimed:[149]

It should also be noted that there is a small body of toxicological evidence demonstrating mortality in rodents exposed to PM (e.g., Killingsworth et al. 1997).

Curious as to what this "small body of toxicological evidence" was as represented by "Killingsworth et al 1997," I pulled the study and found that the rats did not die because they were exposed to a massive amount of PM2.5. Instead, they died because they were first treated with a chemical called monocrotaline, a poison used to give laboratory animals lung disease.[150] The Killingsworth study is so unimportant to PM2.5 science that it is not even mentioned in EPA's most recent 1071-page scientific assessment of PM2.5 issued in 2009.[151]

It was no wonder, then, that EPA immediately qualified its "small body of toxicological" evidence assertion of its 2012 PM2.5 rulemaking with the following:

Overall it is not surprising that lethality is not induced in more toxicological research, as these types of studies do not readily lend themselves to this endpoint.

With respect to the EPA's human experiments, there is not even a "Killingsworth" level of evidence that PM2.5 causes death. Despite testing very high exposures of PM2.5 on likely more than a thousand human guinea pigs, no one was killed—even when PM2.5 was tested on allegedly vulnerable populations like the sick and the elderly. EPA admitted to the court during the human testing lawsuit that the purpose of its human experiments was to provide biological plausibility for the hypothesis that PM2.5 could kill. But the human experiments failed to do so as not a single adverse health effect attributable to PM2.5 occurred, let alone a death, was reported.

None of this is surprising when you consider what is known about real-world exposures to PM2.5.

CHAPTER 27

Smoked Out

In the end, you don't need to be a statistician, epidemiologist, toxicologist, or scientist of any kind to comprehend the absurdities of the EPA's PM2.5 claims. You just need to think about the occurrence of PM2.5 in our everyday lives. Reality proves that PM2.5 does not kill any one on either a short-term or a long-term basis.

Recall that the physical entity we are talking about is just very small soot and/or dust that people unavoidably inhale all the time. But the EPA has successfully removed that dust and soot from the realm of mundane by labeling it "PM2.5," as if it were some special toxin that only emanated from manmade sources that the EPA says can and ought to be regulated. But all this is a fiction that is readily debunked when PM2.5 is viewed in the context of the real world.

My favorite slayer of the EPA's PM2.5 myth is tobacco smoke. If you've ever smoked a cigarette (or anything else) and survived, you've debunked the EPA's PM2.5 claims all by yourself. But we can't leave it there. The actual facts are so much more fun.

You may recall that one of the lead physicians in the EPA human experiments was a physician named Andrew Ghio. He was the lead author for the case report on the 58-year-old woman who experienced atrial fibrillation during the EPA experiment on her. In addition to drawing my attention to the EPA's ghastly experiments, I am indebted to Ghio for this statement made in a study of his published in the *American Journal of Respiratory and Critical Care:*[152]

> *Smoking one cigarette exposes the human respiratory tract to between 10,000 and 40,000 [millionths-of-a-gram] of particulate matter . . . The composition of cigarette smoke [particulate matter] is comparable to that of other particles generated through combustion of carbonaceous material . . .*

So Ghio has informed us that a smoker may inhale somewhere between 10,000 to 40,000 millionths-of-a-gram of PM2.5 in the time it takes to smoke a single cigarette, or roughly 5 to 10 minutes. To put this in perspective, the average level of PM2.5 in U.S. outdoor air is around 10 millionths-of-a-gram per cubic meter and the average non-smoking adult inhales about a cubic meter of air per hour.

So someone inhaling typical U.S. outdoor air would inhale about 10 millionths-of-a-gram of PM2.5 per hour or about 1 millionth of a gram every 6 minutes or so. That means that while smoking, a smoker roughly inhales PM2.5 at a rate 10,000 to 40,000 times greater than a nonsmoker—and may do so many times per day. Gen. Dwight D. Eisenhower famously smoked as many as four packs of unfiltered cigarettes per day during World War II. The PM2.5 inhaled by Eisenhower and such heavy smokers in a single day is off the charts. We have all seen smokers in action, yet not one of us has ever seen a smoker keel over and die while smoking or shortly thereafter, despite the incredible amount of PM2.5 being inhaled. Moreover, there is no example in the scientific literature of anyone dying merely from inhaling so much PM2.5 from a cigarette over such a short period of time. Keep in mind that I am not talking about the potential adverse health effects of long-term smoking which are considerable. We are merely talking about people surviving after smoking a single cigarette.

One of the oldest principles of toxicology, the study of poisons, is that "the dose makes the poison." If, as according to EPA there is no safe level of PM2.5 inhalation, then single cigarettes ought to be tools of suicide. Each cigarette ought to be one's last, if the EPA is correct about PM2.5.

If you're still not convinced, there's more.

If you're worried about PM2.5, marijuana joints make cigarettes look safe. Smoking a marijuana joint, due to the lack of a filter, exposes the smoker to as much as four times more PM2.5 than a cigarette—that is as much as 160,000 millionths-of-a-gram of PM2.5.[153] That's about two years worth of PM2.5 from typical outdoor air inhaled all at once. Yet many states are moving to legalize pot smoking while the EPA futilely tries to remove PM2.5 from the environment at great expense to society. The marijuana legalization movement would, of course, be stopped dead in its tracks if PM2.5 killed the way the EPA claims.

Marijuana's PM2.5 has essentially been approved by the U.S. Food and Drug Administration for physicians to prescribe to terminally ill patients. The purpose is not to kill them, but to ease their pain and improve their quality of life. Though the EPA would likely consider the terminally ill to be a population "vulnerable" to the supposedly lethal effects of PM2.5, a single marijuana joint has yet to kill any one of them.

Then there are hookah bars, establishments where patrons smoke a syrupy tobacco through a water pipe. The National Institutes of Health described the hookah bar experience as follows:[154]

Puffing tobacco through waterpipes, a Middle Eastern tradition, is exploding in global popularity, including among American college students. Many assume these gadgets, also known as hookahs, provide a safer, cleaner way of using tobacco. Yet NIH-funded researchers have determined the smoke from these pipes contains an array of harmful chemicals, including ten times more carbon monoxide than the smoke from a single cigarette. Hookah smokers take an average of about 100 puffs per session, with each one delivering approximately the same amount of smoke typically consumed from a single ciga-rette, studies show.

At 40,000 millionths-of-a-gram of PM2.5 per cigarette, that would be 4,000,000 millionths-of-a-gram which is the equivalent of breathing more than 45 years worth of outdoor PM2.5 in one evening. But the only deaths I could find related to hookah bars tended to involve the rather large particles more commonly known as bullets.

Finally, there is the EPA's claim that the elderly and sick are the most vulnerable to PM2.5. If you haven't already been disabused of this notion by the use of medical marijuana by the terminally ill, there are still more data.

As incredible as this seems, a fair percentage of smokers keep smoking even after they have suffered heart attack, stroke and/or lung cancer. Although these sick people would clearly be considered by the EPA as especially vulnerable to the effects of PM2.5 in outdoor air, they are oddly enough not so especially vulnerable to much greater amounts of PM2.5 when they smoke.

While epidemiologic studies report that people who continue to smoke after a heart attack die at a rate up to 100 percent greater than people who quit smoking after a heart attack, that increased death rate occurs over the long-term as measured in years. Meanwhile, these supposedly vulnerable-to-PM2.5 persistent smokers are inhaling comparatively massive doses of PM2.5 and surviving.

A study in the Journal of the American College of Cardiology reported that post-heart attack persistent smokers, over a period of 13 years died at a rate about 60 percent greater than did post-heart attack patients that quit.[155] The study reported that every five cigarettes smoked on a daily basis over that 13-year period increased the risk of death by the end of that period by about 20 percent.

If we estimate that each cigarette smoked exposes the smoker to 40,000 millionths-of-a-gram of PM2.5 and that breathing average outdoor air exposes someone to about 200 millionths-of-a-gram per day, then every cigarette smoked is equivalent to inhaling 200 days

worth of outdoor air PM2.5 in about five minutes. Every five cigarettes smoked, then is like inhaling three years worth of outdoor air
PM2.5 in less than one half hour. Although these vulnerable people
are continually inhaling these comparatively massive doses of PM2.5,
they do not die on a scale remotely close to EPA's claims of short-
term death for sick people breathing average outdoor air levels of PM2.5.
Then there are people with serious lung diseases like chronic
obstructive pulmonary disease (COPD) who continue to smoke
even though they need an oxygen tank to breathe. If PM2.5 were as
dangerous as the EPA claimed, these extremely vulnerable people
would most certainly be dying at high rates. But guess what? The
urgent concern with these sick people is not their smoking—it's the
risk of flash burns from accidentally igniting their oxygen tanks.[156]

Not only does the smoking epidemiology debunk the notion
that PM2.5 kills on a short-term basis, it also debunks the claims
that PM2.5 kills on a long-term basis. A good example is a recent
study in the prestigious *New England Journal of Medicine* on the
benefits of quitting smoking. That study reported:[157]

> *Life expectancy was shortened by more than 10 years among
> the current smokers, as compared with those who had never
> smoked. Adults who had quit smoking at 25 to 34, 35 to 44,
> or 45 to 54 years of age gained about 10, nine and six years
> of life, respectively, as compared with those who con-
> tinued to smoke.*

So the study reports that pack-a-day smokers stand to lose, on
average, about 10 years of life expectancy. But the data showed that
if a smoker quits by age 35, that 10 years might be gained back. So
how does this shed light on the EPA's claim that long-term exposure
to PM2.5 can cause death?

Let's assume that life expectancy among non-smokers is 80 years
of age. So a person breathing typical U.S. outdoor air containing
10 millionths-of-a-gram of PM2.5 per cubic meter would inhale

about 7 million millionths-of-a-gram of PM2.5 over the course of 80 years. A pack-a-day smoker who smoked until age 35 years would inhale as much PM2.5 as the non-smoker in addition to another 4.4 billion millionths-of-a-gram of PM2.5 from smoking.[158] So although the nonsmoker and smoker would have the same life expectancy of 80 years, the smoker would have inhaled 625 times more PM2.5 over the course of his lifetime.

A good visual conception of the difference in PM2.5 inhalation between the nonsmoker and smoker is that the nonsmoker would inhale about two one-ounce sugar packets worth of PM2.5 while the smoker would inhale more than a four pound sugar bag's worth of PM2.5 over the courses of their expected 80-year lifetimes. If one can inhale more than four pounds of PM2.5 and have the same life expectancy as someone who has inhaled only one-quarter of an ounce of PM2.5, then PM2.5 must not be at all deadly.

Though somewhat anti-climatic as compared to the case of smoking, the epidemiology on secondhand smoke also debunks the EPA's PM2.5 claims. A 2007 study published in the *Journal of the Air & Waste Management Association* reported on a variety of common exposures to PM2.5 in secondhand smoke. Before we get to their results, it should be pointed out that the researchers believe the PM2.5 from secondhand smoke to be *more* dangerous that the PM2.5 in outdoor air, as follows:[159]

> *The EPA standard [for PM $_{2.5}$] was devised for ambient air pollution, which is likely to have substantially different composition than tobacco smoke pollution. However, because secondhand smoke contains many toxic compounds, including carcinogens, it is likely that, at a given airborne particle concentration, secondhand smoke carries the greater risk.*

The researchers reported outdoor levels of PM2.5 levels within a couple feet of a smoker were as high as 1,000 millions of a gram per cubic meter of air—or more than 28 times greater than the EPA's "safe" level of PM2.5 in outdoor air.

The levels of PM2.5 from secondhand smoke in confined indoor spaces can be even greater. The California Air Resources Board reports that PM2.5 levels from secondhand smoke can reach 4,000 millionths-of-a-gram per cubic meter in a car with the windows up—even with the air conditioning going full blast.[160] Hookah bars have been measured to have on average almost 1,200 millionths-of-a-gram of PM2.5 per cubic meter.[161] Even regular bars that allow smoking can have PM2.5 levels in excess of 300 millionths-of-a-gram per cubic meter.[162]

None of these exposures to secondhand smoke PM2.5 is known to have ever caused a short-term death. Never.

The EPA's own famous (or infamous, depending on your point of view) 1992 risk assessment for secondhand smoke also debunks the EPA's PM2.5 claims.[163] This document was researched and issued several years before EPA proposed to regulate PM2.5. So it represents what the EPA had concluded about PM2.5 before the agency realized that PM2.5 in outdoor air represented a tremendous opportunity for a new, never-ending regulatory program.

In its risk assessment, the EPA concluded that secondhand smoke was statistically associated only with lung cancer—and even that finding, as described earlier, was eviscerated by a federal judge for its scientific, statistical and regulatory corruption. Other health effects to adults that the EPA mentioned in the report included temporary coughing, phlegm production, chest discomfort and reduced lung function. Sudden or short-term death was not at all mentioned as a potential health outcome. This despite the fact that the epidemiology studies included in the risk assessment involved study subjects who not only likely had very heavy exposure to secondhand smoke PM2.5, but in many cases were also smokers or ex-smokers themselves.

None of this is news to the EPA and its PM2.5 researchers. This smoking paradox is such a large hole in the EPA's theory of PM2.5

lethality that EPA-paid researcher C. Arden Pope, of the "Pope study" previously discussed, set about to try to explain it. In a 2009 study, Pope floated the bizarre explanation that the extremely low levels of PM2.5 are acutely lethal while the exponentially greater levels of PM2.5 smokers inhale are somehow far less lethal.[164]

While there are many technical problems with Pope's study, the most important and easiest problem to understand is that there is not another substance known to man that acts this way. Since the advent of modern toxicology about 500 years ago, the basic principle of toxicology is "the dose makes the poison." This means the greater the dose of a substance is, the greater are its poisonous effects. So if low-levels of PM2.5 kill, then high-levels of PM2.5 should kill more. But this is not what is observed in the real world.

The smoking epidemiology is a clear and objective test of the EPA's claims that PM2.5 causes death, in the short-term and the long-term. The EPA's claim obviously fails. While that could be the end of this story, it's not. EPA's PM2.5 claims fail every other test of reality, too.

CHAPTER 28

Working In A Coal Mine

While no other inhalation of PM2.5 comes close to matching the magnitude and intensity of smoking, there is one that comes close, at least in terms of irony—coal mining.

Coal miners are and always have been exposed to immense amounts of mine dust and engine exhaust, much of which is PM2.5.[165] Since the 1970s, federal regulations required that coalmine operators limit the respirable dust level in mines to 2,000 millionths-of-a-gram per cubic meter of air. That 40-year-old standard was arbitrarily "reduced" to 1,500 millionths-of-a-gram per cubic meter of air on August 1, 2016.[166]

This new lower standard is based on a miner working 1,920 hours per year underground for 45 years for a career total of 86,400 hours of exposure to this high level of mine dust. Keep in mind that average U.S. outdoor air only contains about 10 millionths-of-a-grams of PM2.5 per cubic meter of air. So mine air may contain as much as 150 to 200 times as much particulate matter as outdoor air. Over a 45 year career of such exposure, a coal miner will inhale approximately 173 million millionths-of-a-gram of coal mine dust, much of which is PM2.5—which is far in excess of the 7 million millionths-of-a-gram of PM2.5 regular non-smoking people inhale from outdoor air over the course of an 80-year lifespan.

So what are the health consequences for coal miners? Do miners simply drop dead from acute PM2.5 exposure? No, they do not, despite the fact that many of them smoke as well as mine.

As the Mine Safety and Health Administration summarized the health effects to miners of coal mine dust when it tightened the standard in May 2014:

> *The health effects from occupational exposure to respirable coal mine dust consist of interstitial and obstructive pulmonary diseases. Miners develop Coal Workers' Pneumoconiosis (CWP) or nonmalignant respiratory disease (NMRD). There are no specific treatments to cure CWP or NMRD. These chronic effects may progress even after miners are no longer exposed to respirable coal mine dust resulting in increased disability and death. Other complications may follow, such as pulmonary and cardiac failure, that result in total disability and premature death.*

So the health effects of concerns are "chronic," meaning long-term in nature. In contrast to EPA's claim that relatively low outdoor levels of PM2.5 kill in the short-term, as in hours or days, there is no concern or evidence that that levels of PM2.5 as much as 200 times greater are killing miners on a short-term basis. But what about over the long term? Didn't the Mine Safety and Health Administration conclude that these chronic health effects could result in premature death? Yes, but many chronic diseases or conditions often lead or contribute to death.

The inconvenient reality, however, is that coal miners don't die sooner than the average person—despite the miners' other dramatic exposure to PM2.5. A study titled "Mortality Among U.S. Underground Coal Miners: a 23 Year Follow-up" published by federal researchers at the U.S. National Institute for Occupational Safety and Health reported that the death rate for coal miners did not differ in a meaningful way from that of the average U.S. worker.[167] But that's not all.

In this population of 8,899 underground coal miners, 54 percent of the miners were smokers and another 25 percent were former smokers. Only about 20 percent were lifetime non-smokers. The non-smoking coal miners, whose only major exposure to PM2.5 would be from coal mining, had a death rate 25 percent lower than the average U.S. worker. Coal miners who smoked, but stopped at some point had a death rate 18 percent lower than the average U.S. worker. The only coal miners with a death rate higher than the average U.S. worker were the miners who never stopped smoking.

The conclusion, then, is that coal miners are not killed in the long-term by the very high levels of PM2.5 in coalmines. Not to mention that the combination of PM2.5 from coal mine dust and cigarette smoke is not known to have killed any miner ever in the short-term manner the EPA claims for everyday exposures to PM2.5 in outdoor air.

The great irony here is that the coal industry has never defended itself with these facts. Since 2012, the EPA has issued three major regulations against the coal industry that were based on the claim that the comparatively minute amounts of PM2.5 emanated from power plant smokestacks killed tens of thousands of people every year. But the coal industry has surprisingly never tried to defend itself with the fact that if PM2.5 was as lethal as claimed by the EPA, then coal miners would have always been and continue to be dropping like flies.

Another relevant albeit less dramatic occupational exposure to PM2.5 comes from workers exposed to diesel exhaust, which is 95 percent PM2.5. A 2012 study published in the Journal of The National Cancer Institute reported that limestone, potash and salt miners exposed to diesel exhaust at an average of between 45 to 180 millionths-of-a-gram PM2.5 per cubic meter lived longer than the average U.S. worker. [168] Similar results have been reported for other workers including railroad workers[169] and truck drivers.[170] These exposures to PM2.5 pale in comparison to those of coal miners, but in no case is there any sign of an increase in short-term or long-term death rates.

CHAPTER 29

A History of Deadly Air Pollution

So we now know that massive amounts of PM2.5 aren't known to cause death on a short-term or long-term basis. But can't air pollution kill people? Yes, it certainly has in the past. But as revealed in this book for the first time, only under certain circumstances that no longer occur anywhere on the planet, let alone the U.S.

The first major air pollution episode of the 20th century associated with an epidemic of death occurred in Belgium's Meuse Valley from December 1 to December 5, 1930. The Meuse Valley was a heavily industrialized region containing steelworks, zinc smelters, glass manufacturers and fertilizer and explosives plants.[171] During that week, a weather phenomenon known as a temperature inversion occurred that blocked the smokestack emissions from rising and dispersing harmlessly into the atmosphere. By December 4, a thick fog had settled in the Meuse Valley. By the next day, 60 people had died in a town of 3,500 inhabitants. The age range of the victims was 20 years to 89 years with an average age of 62 years.

So what had been the cause of these deaths? There were certainly many possible culprits. Smokestack emissions included particulate matter, carbon dioxide, carbon monoxide, hydrogen gas, hydrogen sulfide, arsine (a gaseous arsenic compound), nitrogen dioxide, ammonia and hydrochloric acid. An investigation was launched the day after the inversion ended and the air had cleared on

December 6, 1930. These investigators did what the EPA has never bothered to do—autopsies.

The investigators determined that all the deaths were caused by irritation of lung tissue. (Recall that EPA places heavy emphasis on PM2.5 causing heart attacks). After ruling out respiratory infections and lack of oxygen as causes of death, the investigators reported:

> . . . *the diffuse superficial mucosal congestion that occurred throughout the respiratory tract down to the bronchioles and lung parenchyma . . . could be attributable to fine irritant particles [which had been inhaled shortly before death].*

Oh no, they were killed by "fine irritant particles?" Doesn't that mean PM2.5? Yes it does. And, no doubt, that is where EPA would like the story to have ended. But it doesn't because that's not the full and true story.

You see, even the Meuse Valley fog investigators—in 1930—knew that carbon particles by themselves were "innocuous." What they concluded was that:

> . . . *fine particles, onto which irritant gases had been adsorbed, had a major role in the noxiousness of the fog.*

So the Meuse Valley fog investigators concluded the actual toxic agent was some gas in the air that, they further hypothesized, had attached itself to the PM2.5 subsequently inhaled. One suspected toxic agent was hydrofluoric acid that was emitted by a local fertilizer plant and had previously affected plants and grazing animals. But the geographic distribution of the deaths did not match up with a single source for the lethal agent.

The investigators eventually determined that sulfur dioxide, produced from widespread and uncontrolled burning of high-sulfur coal, was the main culprit. Because of the temperature inversion over the Meuse Valley, sulfur dioxide concentrations hit 100 milligrams per cubic meter, which is about 473 times higher than the EPA's sulfur dioxide standard. PM2.5 may have possibly helped maintain the sulfur dioxide in the air longer, the investigators hypothesized, but it was certainly not the lethal agent.

The EPA has never been truthful about this episode. In a 1995 staff paper prepared ahead of the agency's 1996 proposal to regulate PM2.5 for the first time, the EPA wrote:[172]

> *Reports of the effects of ambient PM on health date back to the dramatic pollution episodes of Belgium's Meuse Valley, Donora, Pennsylvania and London, England.*

But the Meuse Valley incident is not the only bit of history EPA has tried to rewrite. The two other examples also provide vital insight into when air pollution is lethal.

The air pollution incident that propelled efforts to clean U.S. air occurred in October 1948 in the Pennsylvania town of Donora, situated southwest of Pittsburgh. As in the case of the Meuse Valley, Donora was an industrialized area with a population of about 12,300 located in a valley that became subject to a temperature inversion.

A fog developed in Donora on October 27 and dissipated on October 31. At its peak, it became so dark that the town's streetlights were turned on at noontime. By the time the fog was gone, 17 people had died. Three more fog-related deaths occurred the next week. The ages of those who died ranged between 52 to 84 years with median of 65 years. What caused the deaths?

Autopsies were performed on several of the victims. The results were summarized in the U.S. Public Health Service's report on the incident:[173]

> *The evidence derived by autopsy discloses that the larynx, trachea and bronchi of the first order were affected. Apparently the irritating agent was carried into the lung and exerted its primary effect upon the terminal bronchi, the bronchioles and*

the pulmonary parenchyma. However that agent must have had a low irritating capacity since none of the cases exhibited a degree of hemorrhage, edema, or necrotizing process commonly associated with the inhalation of lethal irritating substances.

So once again, contrary to the EPA's PM2.5 claims, the physical effect that caused the deaths occurred in the lungs. The Public Health Service report on Donora then makes the following remarkable suggestion:

Analogy might be made here with certain war gases. Phosgene, of example, has little effect upon the upper respiratory tract. The finer bronchi and lungs undergo an intense edema and congestion during the acute phase of the poisoning. Later, a purulent bronchiolitis supervenes with the spread of exudate for a variable distance into the surrounding alveoli.

The lethal agent at work in Donora, then, might have been a deadly, but ultimately unknown gas. But what about PM2.5? The Public Health Service report went on to state:

The isolated particles discovered within the macrophages and connective tissue framework of the alveolar walls of the cases studies may have some bearing on the mechanism to explain the biological aspects of the incident. Thought in this regard is admittedly speculative. Is it possible that the isolated particles by reason of adsorption might have carried a substance into the lung, thus concentrating an otherwise nonlethal level of that substance present in the atmosphere breathed by the fatal cases? Any answer to that inquiry will obviously be complicated and incomplete by reason of the following: Such isolated particles are present in the lungs of practically all cases having exposure to dust. Their presence as isolated particles rather than as mobilized masses within the lymphatic channels does not preclude deposition through recent inhalation such as might have occurred in the three cases that died during the smog. Again there is no evidence that isolated particles had a local effect which might be expected had they carried an irritating substance into the lung. Furthermore, tissues other than the lung showed no damage due to adsorbed substances possibly released from those particles and distributed systematically.

So death from particulate matter was considered but dismissed from lack of any physiological evidence from the autopsies. The Public Health Service reported concluded:

It appears, therefore, that some substance was present in the atmosphere inhaled, that that substance irritated the lungs and that death occurred in certain individuals who were more vulnerable to low levels of such irritation by reason of preexisting chronic disease unrelated to the incident.

What could that agent have been? The Public Health Service considered a number of suspects including fluoride, chloride, oxides of nitrogen, hydrogen sulfide, calcium oxide and sulfur dioxide and the oxidation it produces. It then concluded:

It does not appear probable from the evidence obtained in the investigation that any one of these substances (irritant or nonirritant) by itself was capable of observing the syndrome observed. However, a combination of two or more of these substances may have contributed to that syndrome.

It is well known that one substance may influence the physiologic action of another and it is possible that there was a summation of the action of the individual irritant constituents which produced an effect greater than would be anticipated for any one of the individual constituents. Moreover, there is evidence which indicates that the effect of irritant gases can be enhanced by adsorption on particulate matter. In addition to enhanced action, gases may be carried deeper into the respiratory tract than they would normally be carried in the absence of such particulate matter. This action would then carry the noxious substance into the lower levels of the respiratory system where the more damaging effects would be produced.

It is known that irritant gases exert their effect in the respiratory tract depending largely on their solubilities; that is, compounds which are highly soluble exert their effect in the upper respiratory tract while compounds which are less soluble exert their primary action in the deeper parts of the lung. A gas, therefore, such as sulfur dioxide which would normally exert its primary action in the upper part of the respiratory tract might produce more serious effects if it were transported to the deeper parts of the lungs, as for example, by particulate matter. Both solid particulate matter and liquid particulate matter (fog) were present in the atmosphere in large quantities during the October 1948 episode.

Another influencing factor to be considered is carbon dioxide which was probably a significant contributor to the overall atmospheric pollution load. Because carbon dioxide is a respiratory stimulant, it may have contributed to the effects produced by the other contaminants by virtue of the increase in depth of respiration which it induces.

It seems reasonable to state, on the basis of the previous discussion, that while no single substance was responsible for the October 1948 episode, the syndrome could have been produced by a combination, or summation of the action, of two or more of the contaminants. Sulfur dioxide and its oxidation products, together with particulate matter are considered significant contaminants. However, the significance of the other irritants as important adjuvants to the biological effects cannot be finally estimated on the basis of present knowledge.

It is important to emphasize that information available

*on the toxicological effects of mixed irritant gases is meager
and that data on possible enhanced action due to adsorption
of gases on particulate matter is limited. Further available
toxicological information pertains mainly to adults in relatively
good health. Hence, the lack of fundamental data on the
physiological effects of a mixture of gases and particulate matter
over a period of time is a severe handicap in evaluating the
effects of atmospheric pollutants on persons of all ages and in
various states of health.*

The takeaway message is that in the absence of a lethal irritant
gas, particulate matter is not known or even suspected to cause harm.

But there was more exculpatory information concerning PM2.5
in the Public Health Service report. During the spring of 1949, the
U.S. Weather Bureau monitored the air quality in Donora to better
understand what it typically contained—and that was a lot of particulate matter.

From 12 air-sampling stations in the Donora area from mid-Feb-
ruary 1949 through late-April 1949, total particulate matter was
measured in the range from 0 to 499 millionths-of-a-gram per cubic
meter 46 percent of the time. We can probably safely assume that
the vast majority of measurements were at the upper end of that
range as monitoring data showed that total particulate matter ranged:
between 500 to 999 millionths-of-a-gram per cubic meter about 32
percent of the time; between 1,000 to 1,499 millionths-of-a-gram
about 10 percent of the time; and ranged between 1,500 to 2,500-
plus millionths-of-a-gram per cubic meter almost 12 percent of the
time. While there was no breakdown regarding what proportion of
these levels represented PM2.5, we can confidently assert that that
proportion was significant, keeping in mind that the initial (1971)
EPA standard for total particulate matter in ambient air was 260
millionths-of-a-gram per cubic meter.[174]

Although Donora's air typically contained a great deal of total
particulate matter, including PM2.5, the Donora residents were not

known to be less healthy than any other neighboring community. The industrialized Donora valley, in fact, had a lower death rate than the rest of the United States, the vast majority most of which likely had much cleaner air.

There is an interesting addendum to the Donora incident that has great relevance to the EPA and its abuse of statistics to advance its PM2.5 claims. In a May 1950 review of the U.S. Public Health Service report on the Donora incident, the *Journal of the American Medical Association* editorialized:[175]

> *There is need to know whether there is an insidious effect on those living their lifetime under an industrially polluted sky. Statistical studies of death rates in industrial cities are not sufficient. The situation requires the best investigative medicine.*

So it has been known for more than 65 years that the statistical nature of epidemiology is insufficient for studying air quality. The EPA knew this, too. That's why the agency undertook the human experiments. But those experiments failed to validate the EPA's claims about PM2.5. But the agency regulated anyway.

CHAPTER 30

Dirty Air, But No Bodies in China

The last epic air pollution episode of the 20th century was the London Smog of December 5-9, 1952. As in the case of the Meuse Valley and Donora incidents, a temperature inversion caused chimney and smokestack emissions to accumulate in the lower atmosphere. The London death rate spiked during the smog event and was noticeably elevated during the next couple of months. There were about 13,000 more deaths during the period December 1952 to March 1953 as compared to the same period the previous year.[176] Although the smog was likely responsible for many of these deaths, there was also a deadly influenza epidemic in London during that time.

While there no doubt was an incredible amount of particulate matter emitted by smokestacks, chimneys and vehicle tailpipes fouling London's air, particulates were not blamed for the deaths. The *British Medical Journal* opined in the smog's aftermath:[177]

> *[Available smog masks] would not put much of a barrier against the sulphur dioxide that is believed to constitute the main danger [of the 1952 London smog].*
>
> *Natural fog consists of small droplets, mainly of water, up to about 100 [millionths of a meter] in size. Smog contains, besides sulphur dioxide and ash particles, sulphuric acid and particles of [oily] distillate. Internal combustion engines, which*

so far have seemed to escape some of the blame that may well be theirs, emit fine carbon particles and traces of lead. The amount of carbon monoxide emitted from motorcars has recently been estimated at 2,000 tons a day in greater London. Smoke pouring from domestic chimneys is such an obvious contributor to the smog pall that critics of it have been apt to overlook the dangers of the gases given off when smokeless fuels are burnt. Such fuels are not the complete solution to the problem for they give off sulphur dioxide and carbon monoxide...

While nothing more than a strong suspicion has fallen on the oxides of sulphur as the chief menace in smog, evidence has been provided ... that healthy adults experience shallower and more rapid respiration and an increased pulse rate after breathing sulphur dioxide for 10 minutes at a concentration of 1 part per million, the effects being more severe with increase of concentration. During the smog last year the maximum concentration of sulphur dioxide was rather over 1 part per million in central London and the mean was about 0.9 parts per million during December 5-9. Healthy adults, however, were not gravely affected: it was those with disease of the heart and lungs who succumbed quickly and the exact cause of their death is not yet known.

That PM2.5 is not fingered as the culprit is not really surprising when you consider that, because of coal burning, London skies were continually filled with PM2.5 without any discernible health effects. Deadly "London fogs" only occurred during weather inversions that trapped noxious gases like sulfur dioxide. The same seems to apply to the 20th century's other episodes of lethal air pollution.

While researchers of the Meuse Valley, Donora and London air pollution incidents could ultimately only hypothesize about what actually caused the observed deaths, we can support their lack of finger-pointing at PM2.5 by considering the air quality crisis in modern day China.

When the cold season arrives and homes start burning coal briquettes in densely populated cities like Beijing, levels of PM2.5 soar to jaw-dropping levels—as high as 1,000 millionths-of-a-gram per cubic meter of air.[178] Even the average level of PM2.5 in Beijing is about 10 times higher than the average levels of PM2.5 in U.S. air. So where are the bodies?

There aren't any. At least none that anyone has tallied, much less produced.

As I reported in a January 2013 commentary in the *Washington Times:*[179]

> *On the worst day so far of the ongoing Chinese air pollution event, Beijing's PM2.5 levels peaked at 886 [millionths-of-a-gram] per cubic meter—an incredible 89 times greater than the U.S. daily average. Based on EPA risk estimates, we should expect the daily death toll in Beijing to have skyrocketed by 89 percent on a same-day and next-day basis. Remember that PM2.5 essentially causes "sudden death," according to the EPA.*
>
> *Beijing has a population of about 19.6 million and an annual death rate of a little more than 500 per 100,000. This means that about 100,000 people die annually in Beijing, or about 274 per day.*
>
> *According to EPA risk estimates, the day the PM2.5 level spiked to 886 [millionths-of-a-gram] per cubic meter, the daily death toll should have increased to about 518 deaths—that is, if what the EPA says about PM2.5 is true.*
>
> *Thus far, however, there is no evidence from China that the EPA's claims about PM2.5 are anywhere close to being true.*
>
> *The Chinese media have reported on four deaths related to the current air pollution crisis. Two Chinese boys were reportedly killed in a train accident caused by visibility problems. Two other people were apparently killed in a car accident, again caused by visibility problems. Yet there are no reports of a spike in deaths caused by breathing the heavily polluted air.*

> *One Beijing hospital reportedly claims to have experienced a 20 percent to 30 percent increase in admission for respiratory ailments—but no deaths have been reported or claimed and deaths are key to EPA's PM2.5 regulations. Even the reported respiratory hospitalizations, to the extent any of them can actually be attributed to poor air quality, would more than likely be due to a genuinely toxic air pollutant or mixture other than mere PM2.5.*

And there is no evidence that the incredible levels of PM2.5 in China increase long-term death rates, either. Consider that, in Washington, D.C., the average annual PM2.5 level is about 10 millionths-of-a-gram per cubic meter and the life expectancy is about 76 years. In contrast, Beijing has about 10 times more PM2.5 in its air on an average annual basis, but life expectancy in Beijing is reportedly more than 81 years.[180] So while Beijing has much more PM2.5 in its air than Washington, D.C., Beijing residents tend to live significantly longer.

Why don't the Chinese drop like flies despite incredibly high levels of PM2.5 in outdoor air? As recognized in 1930 by the investigators of the Meuse Valley incident—ambient levels of PM2.5 are innocuous.

The Chinese PM2.5 paradox has apparently caused panic among the air pollution research community. Without addressing the absence of bodies during acute air pollution episodes in China, air pollution epidemiologists have published studies making claims like PM2.5 in China kills 4,000 people per day.[181] But these researchers didn't do anything approaching an actual scientific investigation. Instead, they estimated PM2.5-related deaths in China by using a mathematical model constructed by the World Health Organization—a model based on the dubious results of the Harvard Six City and Pope studies, which have already been debunked.

CHAPTER 31

Getting Away With It

So how does the EPA get away with its demonstrably false PM2.5 claims? Ironically, a good summation of the EPA's strategy comes from another infamous human experimenter, Auschwitz physician Josef Mengele:

> *The more we do to you, the less you seem to believe we are doing it.*

How is the EPA able to pull this off? How is the agency able to convince itself, Congress and the public that its PM2.5 rubbish is high quality science?

The first problem is that, as the EPA pointed out in the human experiments lawsuit:

> *Nothing in the [Clean Air Act] provides a meaningful standard to evaluate what air pollution the EPA chooses to study or how.*

While Congress may have assumed that the EPA would conduct any needed research in a good faith and in a scientific manner, absent any specific direction, guidance or standards, the EPA has been free to do what it wants. As we have seen, that has included trying to kill or sicken people in its human experiments, hiding key data from the public, statistical malpractice and more.

All this defective research is then given the veneer of "science" by EPA's corrupt peer—or more appropriately, "pal"—review system. Peer review in science is supposed to be the vetting of scientific claims and research by competent and independent professionals. The goal of peer review is not necessarily to weed out wrong science—that often requires more research—but it should be able to weed out obviously poorly conducted research. Why doesn't this happen at EPA?

The EPA spends hundreds of millions of dollars every year providing research grants to external researchers. As of the summer of 2016, the EPA had doled out approximately $581 million for PM2.5-related research.[182] It then pays many of these same researchers to review and validate their own work. I described this problem in a March 2012 commentary in the *Washington Times*:[183]

> *Rep. Joe Barton last week took the first official baby step in exposing the Environmental Protection Agency's corrupt scientific advisory process.*
>
> *In his opening statement at last week's House Energy and Commerce hearing about the EPA's 2013 budget, Mr. Barton of Texas came as close as any Republican ever has to reading EPA Director Lisa P. Jackson the riot act about the agency's ever-increasing contempt for science, economics, Congress and even the Constitution.*
>
> *While much of the aforesaid is widely known but typically left unsaid by timid Congressional Republicans, Mr. Barton also raised an issue that should shock the conscience of anyone concerned about ethics in government: financial conflict-of-interest among EPA science advisers.*
>
> *'I want to discuss the EPA's science and research funding and support activities such as the quality assurance supervisory budget and the committees that monitor the EPA's internal activities,' Mr. Barton told Ms. Jackson.*
>
> *'You fund research with grants to people who also serve on your review committees. Is this a conflict of interest? Almost*

every single member of your Clean Air Science Advisory Committee has been directly or indirectly funded for research. This hand-and-glove policymaking by those appointed to also do your research and being funded by you at the same time is not appropriate. They are often asked to review other research they themselves were a party to on the original research team. How could one possibly expect them to be objective in any way?'

JunkScience.com undertook to put some meat on the bones of what Mr. Barton alleged and discovered that of the seven members of CASAC, six have received or are still receiving substantial sums in the form of research grants from the agency.

According to EPA records, CASAC Chairman Jonathan M. Samet is listed as a principal investigator on grants from the agency totaling $9,526,921. The other CASAC board members have received grants from the EPA: George Allen ($3,907,111); Ana Diez-Roux ($31,343,081); H. Christopher Frey ($2,956,432); G. Armistead Russell ($20,130,736); and Helen Suh ($10,962,364).

Although EPA records do not list seventh board member Kathleen Weathers as a principal investigator receiving any grants from the agency, her employer, the Cary Institute of Ecosystem Studies, is listed as the lead institution in EPA grants totaling $3,570,926.

Other than for Ms. Weathers, these sums don't include any grants awarded to the CASAC members' institutions in which the CASAC member is not listed as the principal investigator. So these sums could just be the tip of the iceberg.

While the above-mentioned information is available to the public, not only do you have to look for it, you've got to first imagine that such immense and obvious conflicts are possible in the first place.

The EPA, after all, dissuades the public from even considering the possibility of this issue, as the first statement on the agency's website is, 'The Clean Air Scientific Advisory Committee

(CASAC) provides independent advice to the EPA Administrator on the technical bases for EPA's national ambient air quality standards.' I suppose it depends on what the meaning of 'independent' is. So exactly what is the 'independent' aspect of a process in which researchers are paid millions of dollars to conduct research and then get to review and rubber-stamp that research so it invariably advances the EPA's own political, regulatory and bureaucratic interests?

Mr. Samet, the CASAC chairman, recently opined in the New England Journal of Medicine *that air-quality rules should be tightened 'for ozone and particulate-matter pollution, because no thresholds have been identified below which there is no risk at all.'*

While there are many individuals not paid by EPA who sit on the various subcommittees of the agency's Clean Air Scientific Advisory Committee, the chairman of each subcommittee is almost always, if not always, an EPA hired gun. Just in case that's not enough to make sure that subcommittees always come out with the "right" answer for the EPA's agenda, the majority of subcommittee members are almost always, if not always, EPA hired guns. The others on the subcommittees don't complain about these insidious arrangements because serving on a committee is considered a professional honor and rocking the boat could have undesirable ramifications for one's career and future funding from the EPA.

Although a spotlight has been turned on the EPA's corrupted system for reviewing science, the agency continues unabated. Let's go back to 1996 when the EPA first proposed to regulate PM2.5. Several months before the EPA actually proposed its PM2.5 rules, a Clean Air Act-mandated independent science advisory group called the Clean Air Science Advisory Committee Particulate Matter Panel (1996 CASAC PM Panel) objected to the EPA's claim that PM2.5 was linked with death.

The 1996 CASAC PM Panel wrote to then-EPA Administrator Carol Browner stating:[184]

[Mortality] does not appear to be unambiguously related to any single pollutant let alone a specific portion of the particulate matter.

At that time in 1996, the panel was comprised of seven members and 14 consultants. Of the seven members, only two had at the time or afterwards received grants from the EPA. Of the 14 consultants, only five had at the time or afterwards received grants from the EPA. In total, then of the 21 individuals involved in the 1996 CASAC PM Panel that reviewed the particulate matter science, only one-third (33 percent) had received grants from the EPA. But as the EPA is not compelled to heed the advice of the CASAC PM Panel, the EPA went ahead and regulated PM2.5 on the basis of mortality anyway.

But the EPA would make sure that future CASAC PM Panels were much more compliant.

Recall that in its 2009 scientific assessment of PM2.5, the EPA determined that any inhalation of PM2.5 can be fatal in as little as a few hours and that PM2.5 can also cause death on a long-term exposure basis.

The 2009 CASAC PM Panel dutifully concluded that:

CASAC recommends 'upgrading' the causal classification for PM2.5 and total mortality as 'causal' for both the short-term and long-term time frames.

Interestingly enough, the 2009 CASAC PM Panel was comprised of seven members and sixteen consultants. Of its seven members, six had at the time or afterwards received grants from the EPA. Of the 16 consultants, 11 had at the time or afterwards received grants from the EPA. So of the 23 individuals on the 2009 CASAC PM

Panel, 17 had at the time or afterwards received grants from the EPA. The problem of the EPA stacking its CASAC PM Panel with its hired guns has only gotten worse.

In November 2015, the EPA formed a new CASAC PM Panel for its new review cycle of the PM2.5 science. Of the panel's 26 members, 24 of them are current of former recipients of EPA grants. The total value of the EPA grants received by these 24 researchers is in excess of $190 million. The panel includes one Douglas Dockery of the Harvard University. Dockery is the lead author of the infamous Harvard Six City that EPA relies on for its PM2.5 claims. For his efforts, Dockery's university has been "awarded" more than $16 million in grants from the EPA. The CASAC PM Panel chair, Ana Diez Roux, has garnered more than $33 million in grants from the EPA during her career. Not to be outdone, however, Columbia University's Patrick Kinney has managed to be on the receiving end of more than $44 million in grants from the EPA.

Rest assured, this new CASAC PM Panel as currently comprised is plenty incentivized to see things the EPA's way. This is despite the fact that both the Clean Air Act and the law under which federal advisory committees like CASAC are formed, known as the Federal Advisory Committee Act, require that the CASAC PM Panel be independent and unbiased.

The EPA's PM2.5 hired guns can be quite shameless in their shilling for the agency. In early May 2015, the media trumpeted a new study by Harvard University and Syracuse University researchers that supposedly verified EPA's claim of its global warming rules saving as many as 57,000 lives every year by reducing PM2.5 emissions from coal-fired power plants.[185] Though such nonsense was nothing new to me, what caught my attention is that the researchers seemed to go out of their way to claim that they were "independent" from the EPA.

The media releases from Harvard and Syracuse expressly stated that the researchers were "independent" and the media coverage from the Associated Press, *New York Times and Washington Post* only mentioned their university affiliations. But there was more. Study co-author Charles Driscoll told the *Buffalo News* that he had "no dog in the fight" and that it was mere coincidence that the model used in the study closely resembled the EPA proposal. About study co-author Jonathan Buonocore of Harvard, *U.S. News and World Report* reported:

> *The EPA, which did not participate in the study or interact with its authors, Buonocore says, roundly welcomed the findings.*

While it only took about 10 minutes of digging to determine that this team of researchers had captured about $45 million in grants from the EPA during their careers—much of which was for PM2.5 research—the best (or worst) was yet to come.[186] Through another Freedom of Information Act request filed with the EPA and, after a few telephone calls with agency staff, I obtained copies of emails between the researchers and the EPA.

The emails revealed that the researchers were, in fact, quite often in contact with the EPA about their study. They even asked the EPA for its help with their study model. Possibly the most appalling email is one in which the lead researcher, Charles Driscoll of Syracuse, hints at the possibility of the EPA showing its appreciation through further finding of a pet project. Writing to EPA official Ellen Kurlansky, Driscoll wrote:[187]

> *Ellen, I hope all is well. We have been busy with our [PM2.5] analysis on the [EPA global warming proposal]. We have been giving briefings to a number of groups. This has been much more successful than I had originally envisioned. There seems to be considerable interest in our analysis.*
>
> *I wanted to see if I could arrange a short call with you to discuss fundraising [for an upcoming conference that I am organizing]. We are making some progress for this meeting but*

it would help if I could raise a little money to help pay for some initial expenses. I wanted to brainstorm with you about how to go about this . . .

Cheers,

Charley

No conflict of interest there.

CHAPTER 32

A Law Unto Itself

So why don't outside parties adversely affected by such obvious corruption—especially businesses and trade groups—complain loudly and constantly? There are many reasons. Businesses and industry groups are often regulated in multiple areas by the EPA. A manufacturer, for example, may be regulated by the EPA for its air emissions, water emissions, hazardous and non-hazardous waste management, products and more. While it is possible to fight and prevail against the EPA on, say, an air issue, the common industry fear is that the EPA will exact revenge in some other area where it has jurisdiction. If you are an industry that requires permits from the EPA, the last thing you want to do is to irritate the EPA and risk the agency venting its anger by delaying, denying, or otherwise sabotaging your permit.

Another problem industries have is that they employ lobbyists, attorneys and consultants whose livelihoods depend in some way or another on remaining on good terms with EPA staff or otherwise not making too many waves. Many lobbyists, attorneys and consultants make their living simply by having relatively easy access to EPA staff. This allows them to obtain inside or pre-public information, as well as to arrange personal meetings and contacts with agency staff. It can be all very cozy for those on the inside.

Lobbyists, attorneys and consultants can be generally divided into two classes: facilitators and interventionists. The facilitators are the vastly larger class of Washington professionals, who specialize in facilitating communications between government and industry. They seldom accomplish anything meaningful for their clients because to do so would risk their own obsolescence. Mostly they spend their time networking, obtaining agency gossip and meeting. The much smaller, if not miniscule, and confrontational interventionist class actually tries to accomplish substantive things for its clients. Sadly, they rarely do because they are not often hired. Interventionists are not afraid of breaking china if that need happen in order to win. But breaking china is not viewed as polite behavior in Washington. Worse, interventionists might win and, thereby, really enrage the EPA.

Industry fear and inability to confront and challenge the EPA is a major problem for the rest of us because industry is the only party with the resources to wage effective war against the EPA. However, few ever do.

While EPA has been able to effectively neutralize industry, it has also effectively employed a network of environmental activists groups and institutions to continually parrot and agitate for its agenda. On the environmental activist side of the ledger, groups like the Environmental Defense Fund, Natural Resources Defense Council and the Sierra Club work closely with the EPA to develop regulations, issue a steady stream of propaganda in favor of the EPA's rules and against the EPA's opponents and often file agency-friendly lawsuits to "force" the agency to regulate more.[188]

One of these sham lawsuits—a process known as "sue-settle"— filed by the American Lung Association produced the settlement by which the EPA agreed to issue the first standards for PM2.5.[189] EPA's 2015 global warming rules aimed at reducing carbon dioxide emissions from coal-fired power plants also resulted from the sue-settle ruse. These groups often agitate for the EPA to continually make more stringent air quality standards, including for PM2.5.

These activist groups and institutions are typically ideologically aligned with the highly-politicized EPA—but they can also be financially aligned. As reported in March 2011 on JunkScience.com, here's how it works:[190]

> *At today's House Energy and Commerce Committee mark-up of the Upton-Inhofe bill to strip EPA of its authority to regulate greenhouse gases, Rep. Lois Capps (D-Calif.) tried to defend the EPA by offering a recent American Lung Association poll that purports to show public opinion favoring the EPA.*
>
> *What Congress needs to know, however, is that the American Lung Association is bought-and-paid-for by the EPA. In the last 10 years, the EPA has given the American Lung Association $20,405,655, according to EPA records.*
>
> *The master-servant relationship between the EPA and [American Lung Association] extends back to at least the early 1990s. As John Merline reported in* Investors Business Daily *(Jan. 28, 1997), between 1990 and 1995, the EPA gave the American Lung Association $5 million—even though the [American Lung Association] was suing the EPA at the time. Although not many grantors give grants to organizations that sue them, at least in the regular world, the EPA likes to be sued by its buddies because such lawsuits invariably expand the agency's powers.*
>
> *So it's not really surprising (or meaningful) that the ALA issued a poll supporting the EPA.*

A Freedom of Information Act request to the EPA produced the following February 8, 2011, email from Paul Billings, a top lobbyist for the American Lung Association, to then EPA chief Lisa Jackson:[191]

> *Attached is the press release we are putting out tomorrow morning together with the attached letter to the House of*

Representatives from 1882 physicians, nurses, respiratory
therapists, certified asthma educators and other health profes-
sionals from all 50 states and DC calling on Congress to 'resist
any efforts to weaken, delay or block a healthier future for all
Americans' and in support of the Clean Air Act.

About one month later, the then-chief of the EPA Office of Air
and Radiation, Gina McCarthy, emailed Billings ahead of an EPA
press conference announcing the Cross-State Air Pollution rule:

Paul – we are pretty excited about the rollout of our proposed
rules. Hoping [the American Lung Association] can stand at
the podium to reinforce the public health message. It seems to
be such great timing on the heels of your report. Should we
talk tomorrow to firm it up?

Billings chummily replied to McCarthy:

Hi Gina – my best window is approximately 11:15 – 2 today.
I would welcome the opportunity to chat.

All of this culminated in a March 16, 2011, joint press conference
between the EPA and the American Lung Association to announce
the PM2.5-related rule.[192]

In July 2011, the American Lung Association produced a television ad featuring a red baby carriage at several Washington DC
locations, including inside a Capitol Hill office building, with a
sound track of a coughing/wheezing infant.[193] The ad was "part of
the Lung Association's Healthy Air Campaign to preserve the EPA's
authority to implement and enforce this 40-year-old, landmark
public health law."[194] Finally, the Senate lobbying disclosure database
reveals that Billings spent quite a bit of time lobbying on behalf of
EPA-related legislation under the guise of the American Lung

Association. So the EPA's $20 million bought the agency the services and credibility of the American Lung Association.

At a June 8, 2011, Senate hearing on air quality and children's health, Sen. John Barrasso (R-WY) confronted the American Lung Association witness with an April 2, 2011 commentary in the Washington Times I wrote spotlighting the American Lung Association's shilling for the EPA.[195] Other than some verbal stumbling and bumbling, the witness offered no explanation.

Congress is too busy, the issues too complex and the EPA and its hirelings too expert at thwarting inquiry and investigation. If a Senator or Representative writes the EPA asking for data or information, they will be fortunate if the EPA responds in a timely fashion or with what was requested—or even at all. Incredibly, Congress has even subpoenaed the EPA (on secret science of PM2.5) to no avail.[196]

Congressional hearings are often disappointing and fruitless because the EPA witnesses dodge and evade without having to provide any meaningful answers. Members of Congress limit themselves to five minutes of questions at a time for witnesses, which is simply not enough time for an in-depth probing of issues. A veteran pro-EPA witness can easily filibuster away a Member's five minute period. Members of Congress are (understandably) typically not well-versed in the intricacies and history of PM2.5 and so are easy to confuse or otherwise thwart.

Many Members of Congress have toyed with the idea of slashing the EPA's budget or entirely withholding funding for targeted programs. While the EPA's budget was reduced in 2015 by about 19 percent from its 2010 peak of $10.3 billion, this has had precious little effect on the agency's regulatory virulence or reliance on junk science. Although provisions to withhold funding for the EPA are often introduced, final bills passed by the House and Senate never ultimately contain any serious budget cuts that might even remotely slow down or curb the agency.

Possibly the saddest Congressional spectacle is when Members try to criticize the EPA while simultaneously asking favors of the agency. Sometimes Members ask the EPA to expedite permits for constituents. Sometimes they ask for the EPA to provide grants to their states—ironically from monies allocated by Congress to the EPA. They might ask for some regulatory process or local permit to be expedited. Whatever the favor, it tempers their ability and interest in pursuing the agency for whatever wrongs it habitually commits.

The EPA has become quite simply a part of the federal government that is a law unto itself. It holds itself above the rules of science and, worse, above the rules of law, even where there is some relevant statutory language. Between its political and ideological bent and fat wallet, the EPA has established an enormous base of support it can call on whenever threatened. It has gotten away with the PM2.5 charade because no one has ever seriously tried to put a stop to it. Even Republican presidents have been afraid to actually do anything to the EPA. Like the U.S. entitlement system, the EPA has become a third rail of politics. It doesn't have to be this way.

CHAPTER 33

Overhauling EPA

Fixing the EPA is no easy task. In fact, it is likely impossible given the political and media power of those threatened by reining in the EPA. It would take a knowledgeable and determined president, super majorities in both houses of Congress and an educated and apolitical judiciary to rid ourselves of the blight on science, the economy and society that the EPA has become. Nevertheless, for those brave souls who might be willing to engage, many options exist.

Ban EPA's use of 'secret science'

First, the EPA's practice of hiding raw scientific data from public scrutiny—that is, "secret science"—must end. If research is relied upon to issue expensive and burdensome regulations, then all of the scientific research underlying their justification must be verified and validated. Mere publication of a study in a scientific or medical journal, however prestigious that journal may be, does not mean that the researchers' conclusions have been verified and validated. If nothing else, peer review may be little more than "pal" review. Research claims can best be scrutinized by those skeptical of the claims and skeptics will need access to the raw data and methods.

The EPA's defenders have opposed Congressional efforts to end the agency's reliance on secret science by claiming, among other things, that to do so would result in personal medical information being released and study subject identities becoming known. This is entirely false, if not absurd.

First, no bona fide researcher is interested in such information since it has no particular scientific value. Next, personal identification data can be easily omitted from death certificates and other records. The state of California already does this. That's how I was able to obtain over two million death certificates from the state in order to do the California PM2.5 study. The California death certificates contained only the key information needed for analysis, including age, date of death, zip code of residence at time of death and cause of death. Name and street address would not have been useful even if provided. So the specter of some breach of medical privacy is a bogus argument.

The heart and soul of the scientific method includes the ability to replicate research results independently. EPA-funded researchers repeatedly reporting the same or similar results does not fill this bill, especially when they can be assured that the agency will help them hide their data from challenge.

End the EPA's corrupt peer review system

Next, the EPA's corrupt peer review process must be brought to an end. The agency cannot be allowed to pay researchers for biased results and then to pay those same researchers to review and rubber-stamp their own work. Imagine if a chief of police was also the judge and prosecutor in a criminal trial and that the jury was comprised of the arresting officer's colleagues. Would that be a fair means of arriving at the guilt or innocence of the accused? But that is what the EPA's peer review system is like. Now imagine that the accused's lawyer was not allowed to scrutinize the evidence submitted by the prosecution, as in the case of EPA's secret science. Would that be a reliable system of arriving at the truth? Of course, not—and so neither is the EPA's corrupt, rubberstamping system of science review boards.

Get EPA out of scientific research

Another important reform is the separation of the EPA from science. The EPA only funds researchers it knows can be relied upon to deliver the results it wants. As explained earlier, I discovered this fact-of-life early in my career when the pro-EPA Clinton administration political staff at the Department of Energy blacklisted me from future work because they didn't like the results of my study on the respective roles of science and politics in the setting of environmental policy. As far as the EPA is concerned, scientists are with it or they are against it. If a scientist is not with the EPA, then he should look elsewhere for research funding. This issue can be thought of as one of academic freedom—and the EPA has no use for that.

Require realistic cost-benefit analysis

Legitimate, independent and reality-based cost-benefit analysis should be mandated for the EPA's proposed regulations. While the concept of cost-benefit analysis is not new, it is rarely done properly. A major shortcoming of the EPA's cost-benefit analyses is that the EPA has figured out how to cook the books so as to produce imaginary benefits that are always greater than the real world costs. PM2.5 is the perfect example of this.

As mentioned earlier, the EPA estimated that the benefit of two of its anti-coal rules—the Cross-State Air Pollution Rule and the Mercury Air Transport Standard—included up to 46,000 lives saved per year yielding an estimated $380 billion every year in health benefits. Considering that the coal industry contribution to the U.S. gross domestic product is "only" on the order of about $225 billion per year, if EPA's benefits estimate were even partially true, it would actually make sense to just shut down the coal industry entirely and profit even more from the economic value of the lives saved.

But as demonstrated here, no lives will be saved by the EPA's rules and the actual benefits are closer to zero. So the estimated costs of the two rules, which are on the order of tens of billions of dollars, suddenly look to be as silly as burning money for no purpose. Even if the cost estimates turn out to be wrong by a factor of say 50 percent or more, it is obviously silly to force businesses and society to spend billions dollars for zero or near-zero benefit.

The EPA assumes that each life "saved" is worth about $10 million—even if someone was 100 years old and PM2.5 was slated to kill him on Tuesday ahead of his natural death on Thursday. This is clearly nonsensical. Compare it to the life of an 18-year old soldier killed in combat, which the U.S. government values at a mere $400,000. (That is the "death gratuity" paid by the U.S. government to the soldier's survivors.) Next, the $10 million figure, as explained earlier, is arrived at through the entirely arbitrary and dubious methodology of willingness-to-pay. It is a mockery of polling to claim that a survey can show that people are willing to pay, say $100, to reduce their chance of premature death by 0.001 percent.

Another problem with the EPA's cost-benefit analysis is that the agency never considers the possibility that its scientific assumptions are incorrect. I have shown here that PM2.5 has not killed anyone. But EPA has never even considered the possibility that it is entirely wrong about PM2.5. The EPA estimated the combined benefits of the Cross-State Air Pollution Rule and Mercury Air Transport Standard to be 18,000 to 46,000 lives saved per year with a corresponding monetized valuation of between $150 billion to $380 billion per year. But what if zero lives were saved? The ranges of lives saved and monetized benefits would then start at zero rather than 18,000 and $150 billion, respectively. And what if zero-lives-saved was far more probable than the EPA's assumption of any lives saved? A graph of the probability density function would be even more revealing of the likely outcomes, if not downright embarrassing for the EPA.

Requiring realistic cost-benefit analysis leads us right into the next reform—Congressional approval of major or expensive regulations. President Reagan's 1981 Executive order on cost benefit analysis required that proposed regulations costing $100 million or more had to be reviewed and approved by the White House Office of Management and Budget. Since 1981, Reagan's Executive Order has been rescinded and replaced with other lesser polices and the Office of Management and Budget has been essentially castrated by the Obama administration. So there is no watchdog ensuring that the EPA's regulations produce more benefits than they cost. Congress should pick up the slack. After all, it is its Constitutional duty.

Require affirmative Congressional approval of major EPA rules

There is a principle of U.S. law called the nondelegation doctrine, which holds that Congress cannot delegate its legislative powers to executive branch agencies. But Congress nevertheless long ago turned over the keys of the U.S. economy to the EPA by allowing the agency to issue laws in the form of regulations with essentially no meaningful oversight. Congress ought to recapture some of its authority by requiring that major regulations—say those costing more than $100 million annually or those that have some inordinate burdensome effect on individuals and businesses—must be affirmatively approved by Congress. This would restore some of Congress's wrongly delegated legislative power and also spotlight major EPA regulations for what they are—politics fueled by political science.

Expand judicial review of EPA rules

U.S. environmental laws have been written, for the most part, by radical environmentalists for the exclusive benefit of radical environmentalists. As a result, it is comparatively easy for environmental groups to get the EPA into federal court to force the agency to adhere to some mindless timetable or mindlessly tighten some standard. The ease with which environmentalists can sue the EPA has led to the aforementioned sue-settle phenomenon in which environmentalists and the EPA do a lawsuit kabuki that usually winds up costing other people (read "businesses and the public") money, jobs, property and other rights and privileges for no net benefit.

People and businesses actually harmed by the EPA have a much more difficult time getting EPA into court—witness our human experiments lawsuit. In that case, the federal judge ruled that only people who didn't know they were being harmed had the right to sue the EPA. How is that supposed to work? Then there is the case of the EPA's PM2.5-related Mercury Air Transport Standard, which was proposed in 2011. By the time the Supreme Court overturned the rule in 2015, the damage to the coal industry had already been done. The EPA's chief Gina McCarthy shockingly laughed off the Supreme Court's rebuff of the rule:[197]

The majority of power plants have already decided and invested in a path to achieving compliance with those mercury and air toxic standards. So we are well on our way to delivering the toxic pollution reductions that people expected.

Then there is the property rights case of Sackett v. EPA. Chantell and Michael Sackett owned a 0.63 acre undeveloped lot of land in Idaho. When they filled in part of their lot in preparation for building a home in 2007, the EPA swooped in, accused them of illegally filling in their land without a permit and began fining them $32,500 per day. When the litigation ended in a unanimous Supreme Court decision in favor of the Sacketts, it was 2012. Yet the Supreme Court win only allowed the Sacketts another day in court with EPA, which is where they remain as of 2016.

So courtroom wins against EPA are time-consuming, expensive and often incomplete. At best, they are pyrrhic victories. Laws need to be changed so that parties aggrieved by EPA have a meaningful opportunity to challenge those laws in a timely and cost-effective manner.

Cut EPA's budget and devolve responsibilities to states

Considering that there is no actual law that created the EPA, it is amazing what a monster agency it has grown into. President Nixon formed the EPA by Executive Order in December 1970 as a sop to anti-war activists. Environmental duties managed by other federal agencies were consolidated into a single agency. The numerous environmental laws that have since been written simply acknowledge the EPA's *de facto* existence.

In 1970, the concept of environmental protection was still a new one. States had not recognized the concept, much less consolidated their various environment-related functions into a single organization. Much has changed over the past 46 years. Not only do states now have unified departments of environmental protection, in fact, most environmental protection activities now are conducted by states. As early as 2002, the administration of President George W. Bush estimated the role of states:[198]

> *Currently, the States enforce most environmental laws through delegated State programs. It is estimated that more than 80 percent of environmental enforcement actions and more than*
>
> *97 percent of environmental inspections are done by the States.*

While there probably are some interstate and international issues in which a federal environmental protection agency could still have a role, the reality is that much of today's EPA could be vaporized and no one, except some bureaucrats and EPA-dependent businesses, would be the worse off. Most environmental issues are local and should be managed that way. A less powerful and less abusive EPA could serve to help address other issues that are beyond a state's jurisdiction or capabilities.

Update environmental laws to reflect today's conditions

Earth to Congress: It is no longer 1970. Laws like the Clean Air Act and the Clean Water Act were written in the 1970s when no one really knew much about environmental protection, except that people wanted and could afford a cleaner environment. So laws were passed, clean up and regulation began and by 1990, the U.S. environment had been vastly improved and made about as clean as made economic sense.

My career on environmental issues began the very month that President George H.W. Bush signed the Clean Air Act Amendments of 1990, a major reform of the Clean Act Air that had the unfortunate effect of removing science from the law. No longer would air emissions standards be set based on health risks as determined by science. Instead, they would be based on what could be accomplished with technology, even if that technology was way more than the science justified. Anyway, since that time, the EPA take action that discernibly or meaningfully improves public health or the environment.

A particular problem has been the Clean Air Act which, with its frenzied 1960s activist mentality, requires that EPA review air quality standards, such as for PM2.5, every five years and adjust them as appropriate. This has turned into a periodic ritual in which the EPA continually tightens the air quality standards without reviewing them to see whether the prior tightening made any difference or whether any new benefits will accrue from further regulation. EPA has decided in the case of PM2.5 that there is no safe level of PM2.5 in the air and each review of the PM2.5 standard must therefore produce a more stringent standard. This is a waste of time, effort and money.

The Clean Air Act only requires that the air we breathe be safe. It does not require that the air be pristine and without substances other than nitrogen, oxygen and various trace gases. But as EPA has determined that there is no safe level of say, PM2.5 or ozone, the EPA has fabricated its own justification for its mindless, arbitrary and never-ending tightening of air quality standards. Let's update the laws to reflect the clean and safe environment we live in and to reflect all the scientific knowledge we've gained. Let's update the laws so that environmental protection efforts can't be hijacked by those whose goals are other than, or well beyond reasonable environmental protection.

CHAPTER 34

A Final Word

As this book goes to press, the researchers who re-did my California study on PM2.5 are working to have their analysis published. But true to form the EPA's henchmen are trying to stop it. When the study was first submitted to the journal *PLoS One*, a sub-editor rejected the study responding:

> *The issue addressed was laid to rest in the mid 1990s by a large reanalysis report sponsored by [Health Effects Institute]. EPA and other regulatory bodies have long since concluded these associations are causal so I don't think there is much point in going over this again and again.*

So if the issue has been "laid to rest," why did EPA tell the court in our human testing lawsuit that it was conducting its human experiments to provide biological or medical plausibility for its statistical results? And why has the EPA spent hundreds of millions of dollars since the mid-1990s on PM2.5 research that's been "laid to rest." And who's ever heard of a sub-editor rejecting out-of-hand a paper because the issue was supposedly settled?

I'm sure the California study will be published sometime and somewhere, but this mindless, knee-jerk initial rejection of the best-conducted PM2.5 study ever is simply mind-boggling. If someone doesn't like the result, the raw data will be made available so they can do their own analysis and dispute the California study. That's how science should work. Meanwhile, EPA continues to hide its raw data and perpetuate its PM2.5 falsehoods.

In closing, consider this extended excerpt from a 2014 Senate report on the history of the EPA's PM2.5 regulations:[199]

> *The greatness of our unique nation hinges on the fundamental purpose of the government to serve at the will of the people and to carry out public policy that is in the public interest. When it comes to the executive branch, the Courts have extended deference to agency policy decisions under the theory that our agencies are composed of neutral, non-biased, highly specialized public servants with particular knowledge about policy matters. This report will reveal that within the EPA, some officials making critically important policy decisions were not remotely qualified, anything but neutral and in at least one case—the EPA decision making was delegated to a now convicted felon and con artist, John Beale.*
>
> *John Beale is the character from the bizarre tale of the fake CIA agent who used his perch at the EPA to bilk the American taxpayer out of more than a million dollars. Even Jon Stewart, host of the popular* Daily Show, *featured Beale's bizarre tale as 'Charlatan's Web' on his program in December 2013. Before his best friend Robert Brenner hired him to work at the EPA, Beale had no legislative or environmental policy experience and wandered between jobs at a small-town law firm, a political campaign and an apple farm. Yet at the time he was recruited to the EPA, Brenner arranged to place him in the highest pay scale for general service employees, a post that typically is earned by those with significant experience.*
>
> *What most Americans do not know is that Beale and Brenner were not obscure no-name bureaucrats housed in the bowels of the agency. Through his position as head of the Office of Policy, Analysis and Review, Brenner built a "fiefdom" that*

allowed him to insert himself into a number of important policy issues and to influence the direction of the agency. Beale was one of Brenner's acolytes—who owed his career and hefty salary to his best friend.

During the Clinton administration, Beale and Brenner were very powerful members of the EPA's senior leadership team within the Office of Air and Radiation, the office responsible for issuing the most expensive and onerous federal regulations. Beale himself was the lead EPA official for one of the most controversial and far reaching regulations ever issued by the agency, the 1997 National Ambient Air Quality Standards (NAAQS) for Ozone and Particulate Matter (PM). These standards marked a turning point for EPA air regulations and set the stage for the exponential growth of the agency's power over the American economy. Delegating the NAAQS to Beale was the result of Brenner's facilitating the confidence of EPA elites, making Beale the gatekeeper for critical information throughout the process. Beale accomplished this coup based on his charisma and steadfast application of the belief that the ends justify the means.

Concerned about this connection, the Senate Committee on Environment and Public Works (EPW) staff have learned that the same mind that concocted a myriad of ways to abuse the trust of his EPA supervisors while committing fraud is the same mind that abused the deference afforded to public servants when he led the EPA's effort on the 1997 NAAQS.

Brenner was known to have an objective on NAAQS and would have done whatever was necessary to accomplish his desired outcome. Together, Brenner and Beale implemented a plan, which this report refers to as 'EPA's Playbook.' The Playbook includes several tools first employed in the 1997 process, including sue-and-settle arrangements with a friendly outside group, manipulation of science, incomplete cost-benefit analysis reviews, heavy-handed management of interagency

237

review processes and capitalizing on information asymmetry, reinforced by resistance to transparency. Ultimately, the guiding principal behind the Playbook is the Machiavellian principal that the ends will justify the means.

In the case of the 1997 NAAQS, the Playbook started with a sue-and-settle agreement with the American Lung Association, which established a compressed timeline to draft and issue PM standards. This timeline was further compressed when the EPA made the unprecedented decision to simultaneously issue new standards for both PM and ozone. Issuing these standards in tandem and under the pressure of the sue-and-settle deadline, Beale had the mechanism he needed to ignore opposition to the standards—the EPA simply did not have the time to consider dissenting opinions.

The techniques of the Playbook were on full display in the 'Beale Memo,' a confidential document that was leaked to Congress during the controversy, which revealed how he pressured the [White House} Office of Information and Regulatory Affairs to back off its criticism of the NAAQS and forced them to alter their response to Congress in 1997. The EPA also brushed aside objections raised by Congress, the Office of Management and Budget, the Department of Energy, the White House Council of Economic Advisors, the White House Office of Science and Technology Policy, the National Academy of Sciences and the EPA's own scientific advisers—the Clean Air Science Advisory Committee.

These circumstances were compounded by the EPA's 'policy call' to regulate PM2.5 for the first time in 1997. PM2.5 are ubiquitous tiny particles, the reduction of which EPA used to support both the PM and ozone NAAQS. In doing so, the Playbook also addressed Beale's approach to the EPA's economic analysis: overstate the benefits and underrepresent the costs of federal regulations. This technique has been applied over the years and burdens the American people today, as up to 80 percent of the benefits associated with all federal regulations are attributed to supposed PM2.5 reductions.

The EPA has also manipulated the use of PM2.5 through the NAAQS process as the proffered health effects attributable to PM2.5 have never been independently verified. In the 1997 PM NAAQS, the EPA justified the critical standards on only two data sets, the Harvard 'Six Cities' and American Cancer Society (ACS II) studies. At the time, the underlying data for the studies were over a decade old and were vulnerable to even the most basic scrutiny. Yet the use of such weak studies reveals another lesson from the EPA's Playbook: shield the underlying data from scrutiny.

Since the 1997 standards were issued, the EPA has steadfastly refused to facilitate independent analysis of the studies upon which the benefits claimed were based. While this is alarming in and of itself, this report also reveals that the EPA has continued to rely upon the secret science within the same two studies to justify the vast majority of all Clean Air Act regulations issued to this day. In manipulating the scientific process, Beale effectively closed the door to open scientific enquiry, a practice the Agency has followed ever since. Even after the passage in 1999 of the Shelby Amendment, a legislative response to the EPA's secret science that requires access to federal scientific data and President Obama's Executive Orders on Transparency and Data Access, the EPA continues to withhold the underlying data that originally supported Beale's efforts.

After President Clinton endorsed the 1997 NAAQS and the agency celebrated their finalization, Beale became immune to scrutiny or the obligation to be productive for the remainder of his time at the agency. Similarly, the product of his labors have remained intact and have been shielded from any meaningful scrutiny, much the same way Beale was protected by an inner circle of career staff who unwittingly aided in his fraud. Accordingly, it appears that the agency is content to let the American people pay the price for Beale and the EPA's scientific insularity, a price the EPA is still trying to hide almost twenty years later.

After reaching the pinnacle of his career at the agency in 1997 and facing no accountability thereafter, Beale put matters on cruise control and enjoyed the lavish lifestyle that the highest paid EPA employee could afford, producing virtually no substantive work product thereafter. For Beale's successes in the 1997 NAAQS process, Beale was idolized as a hero at the agency. According to current EPA Administrator, Gina McCarthy, 'John Beale walked on water at the EPA.' This unusual culture of idolatry has led EPA officials to blind themselves to Beale's wrongdoing and caused them to neglect their duty to act as public servants. As such, to this day the EPA continues to protect Beale's work product and the secret science behind the agency's NAAQS and PM claims.

On December 18, 2013, John Beale was sentenced to 32 months in prison and fined almost $900,000 for defrauding taxpayers largely for pretending to be a CIA agent while working for the EPA. Unfortunately, neither Beale nor anyone else connected with the EPA has yet paid any sort price for defrauding us with costly, job-killing, economy-stifling PM2.5 junk science. But that day of reckoning must come.

Endnotes

[1] *See* BBC News, Spurious Correlations: Margarine Linked to Divorce? May 26, 2014.

[2] *See* Rethinking Risk (Editorial), *Wall Street Journal*, December 6, 1994.

[3] *New York Times*, Congressional Roundup; Backed by Business, G.O.P. Takes Steps To Overhaul Environmental Regulations, February 10, 1995.

[4] For a more complete discussion on PM, see U.S. Environmental Protection Agency, Review of the National Ambient Air Quality Standards for Particulate Matter: Policy Assessment of Scientific and Technical Information—OAQPS Staff Paper, EPA R-452 \R-96-013 (June 1996).

[5] *See* 61 *Federal Register* 65638-6571, December 13, 1996. For a detailed discussion of the origins of the rule *see* U.S. Senate Committee on Environmental and Public Works Minority Staff Report, EPA's Playbook Unveiled: A Story of Fraud Deceit and Secret Science, March 19, 2014.

[6] Milloy SJ and Gough M, The EPA's Clean-Air-ogance, *Wall Street Journal*, January 7, 1997.

[7] Dockery, D.W. et al., An association between air pollution and mortality in six U.S. cities, New England Journal of Medicine, 329:1753–1759.

[8] Pope, C.A. et al., Particulate air pollution as a predictor of mortality in a prospective study of U.S. adults, American Journal of Respiratory and Critical Care Medicine 151: 669–674.

[9] U.S. General Accounting Office, Problems in Air Quality Monitoring System Affect Data Reliability, 82-101, September 22, 1982.

[10] U.S. Centers for Disease Control and Prevention, Trends in Current Cigarette Smoking Among High School Students and Adults, United States, 1965–2011.

[11] Pope A et al., Cardiovascular Mortality and Exposure to Airborne Fine Particulate Matter and Cigarette Smoke Shape of the Exposure-Response Relationship, Circulation 120: 941-948.

[12] Raoof S, A systematic review of secondhand smoke exposure in a car: Attributable changes in atmospheric and biological markers. *Chronic Respiratory Disease*, 12(2): 120-31.

[13] 61 *Federal Register*, at 65641.

[14] Investor's Business Daily, EPA's Case of the Missing Data Industry Can't Get Numbers on the New Pollution Rule, February 21, 1997.

[15] *Id.*

[16] 61 *Federal Register* 38651, July 18, 1997.

[17] Roberts D, Obama's environmental team is centered around a long-time Gore acolyte, Grist.org, December 12, 2008.

[18] *Id.*

[19] Omnibus Appropriations Act for FY1999, P.L. 105-277.

[20] 67 FR 8452, February 22, 2002.

[21] *Salt Institute v. Leavitt*, 440 *F.3d* 156.

22 *See* Millner C, What candidate Obama said about coal, San Francisco Chronicle, June 3, 2014.

23 Milloy S, EPA's Clean Air Act: Pretending air pollution is worse than it is, JunkScience.com, March 9, 2011.

24 42 *U.S.C.* § 7409 (b)(1).

25 U.S. Environmental Protection Agency, FACT SHEET: The Cross-State Air Pollution Rule: Reducing the Interstate Transport of Fine Particulate Matter and Ozone, July 18, 2011.

26 U.S. Environmental Protection Agency (Office of Air and Radiation), Regulatory Impact Analysis for the Federal Implementation Plans to Reduce Interstate Transport of Fine Particulate Matter and Ozone in 27 States; Correction of SIP Approvals for 22 States, June 2011.

27 Health Effects Institute, Reanalysis of the Harvard Six Cities Study and the American Cancer Society Study of Particulate Air Pollution and Mortality, July 2000.

28 Milloy S, Show us the Bodies, EPA, *Washington Times*, July 20, 2011.

29 See U.S. Government Printing Office, Lights Out: How EPA Regulations Threaten Affordable Power and Job Creation, Hearing before the Subcommittee on Regulatory Affairs, Stimulus Oversight and Government Spending of the Committee on Oversight and Government Reform, House Of Representatives, One Hundred Twelfth Congress, First Session, July 26, 2011, Serial No. 112-74.

30 Goldman L, Standing Up for Clean Air Laws (Letter), *Washington Times*, July 26, 2011.

31 Goldman L, Attn Steve Milloy: I've Seen the Bodies, MomsCleanAirForce.org, July 26, 2011.

32 *See* National Library of Medicine, Biography for Dr. Lynn R. Goldman.

33 *See* http://junkscience.com/2011/07/29/show-me-the-bodies-challenge-unnerves-enviros/comment-page-1/#comment-4460.

34 Enstrom JE, Fine Particulate Air Pollution and Total Mortality Among Elderly Californians, 1973–2002, Inhalation Toxicology, 17:803–816.

35 Ghio AJ *et al.*, Case Report: Supraventricular Arrhythmia after Exposure to Concentrated Ambient Air Pollution Particles, *Environmental Health Perspectives*, 120(2): 275–277.

36 The 24-hour standard is defined as the "24-hour average concentrations of PM2.5 mass measured from midnight to midnight from suitable monitors." 40 *Code of Federal Regulations*, Part 50, Appendix N.

37 Milloy, S, EPA show us a body? JunkScience.com, September 15, 2011.

38 See U.S. Government Printing Office, Regulatory Reform Series, Part 7: The EPA's Regulatory Planning, Analysis and Major Actions, Hearing Before the Subcommittee on Oversight and investigations of the Committee on Energy and Commerce House Of Representatives, One Hundred Twelfth Congress, First Session, Serial No. 112-87.

39 U.S. Centers for Disease Control and Prevention, Deaths: Final Data for 2011.

40 American Cancer Society, National Cancer Act Marks Milestone, December 22, 2011.

[41] Letter from Harold Zenick, Director, National Health and Environmental Effects Research Laboratory, U.S. Environmental Protection Laboratory to Steven Milloy, Subject: Freedom of information Act Request No: HQ-FOI-02235-11, November 21, 2011.

[42] Whitman v. American Trucking Association, 531 U.S. 457 (2001).

[43] *See*, Federal Focus, Toward Common Measures: recommendations for a Presidential Executive order on Environmental Risk Assessment and Risk Management Policy, Washington, DC, June 14, 1991.

[44] 46 *Federal Register* 13193.

[45] *See* 58 *Federal Register*, Presidential Documents, October 4, 1993.

[46] *See* 61 *Federal Register* 65638, at 65668.

[47] *See* Heritage Foundation, Can No One Stop the EPA? July 8, 1997.

[48] U.S. Environmental Protection Agency, The Benefits and Costs of the Clean Air Act from 1990 to 2020, Final Report – Rev. A, April 2011.

[49] U.S. Environmental Protection Agency, Combined National and State-level Health Benefits for the Cross-State Air Pollution Rule and Mercury and Air Toxics Standards, EPA-452/R-11-014, December 2011.

[50] U.S. Environmental Protection Agency, The Benefits and Costs of the

Clean Air Act: 1990 to 2020, August 2010.

[51] Milloy S, Did Obama's EPA relaunch the Tuskegee experiments? *Washington Times*, April 24, 2012.

[52] *See* U.S. Centers for Disease Control and Prevention, The Tuskegee Timeline, September 24, 2013.

[53] *See* http://www.hhs.gov/ohrp/humansubjects/commonrule/.

[54] Email from Sean Philpot to Steve Milloy, Re: Did Obama's EPA relaunch Tuskegee experiments, April 25, 2012.

[55] Email from Warren Lux to Steve Milloy, Re: Referral from Sean Philpot, May 2, 2012.

[56] EPA Order 1000.17, Section 4(c).

[57] Email from [Name withheld on request] to Steve Milloy, EPA Human testing, October 2, 2012.

[58] Cascio WE, Air pollution studies important to health, *Washington Times*, May 1, 2012.

[59] Letter from Steve Milloy to Arthur A. Elkins, Jr., May 14, 2012

[60] U.S. Environmental Protection Agency, Integrated Scientific Assessment for Particulate Matter, EPA/600/R-08/139F, p. 6-182, December 2009.

[61] *See* Samet JM, The Clean Air Act and Health—A Clearer View from 2011, *New England Journal of Medicine*, 365:198-201, July 21, 2011.

[62] 76 *Federal Register* 48208, at 48309.

[63] U.S. Environmental Protection Agency, Integrated Scientific Assessment for Particulate Matter, EPA/600/R-08/139F, p. 7-68, December 2009.

[64] 541 *F.2d* 1, *certiorari denied* June 14, 1976 (96 *S.Ct.* 2662, 2663).

[65] *Glasetter v. Novartis*, 252 *F.2d* 986, 992 (2001).

66 Letter from Steve Milloy to Don Wright, Director, Office of Research Integrity, Department of Health and Human Services, May 31, 2012.

67 42 *Code of Federal Regulations* 93.103(b).

68 42 *Code of Federal Regulations* 93.300(b).

69 Letter from David E. Wright, director, Office of Research Integrity to Steven Milloy, June 8, 2012.

70 Bryant A, Welcoming the New Ideas of the Week, *New York Times*, June 18, 2011.

71 U.S. Presidential Commission for the Study of Bioethics, President's Bioethics Commission Releases Results of its Historical Investigation of the 1940s U.S. Public Health Service STD Studies in Guatemala, September 13, 2011.

72 U.S. Presidential Commission for the Study of Bioethics, Moral Science: Protecting Participants in Human Subject Research, December 2011, p. 42.

73 U.S. Presidential Commission for the Study of Bioethics President's Bioethics Commission Releases Report on Human Subjects Protection, December 15, 2011.

74 U.S. Presidential Commission for the Study of Bioethics, Moral Science: Protecting Participants in Human Subject Research, December 2011, p. 60.

75 Letter from Steve Milloy to Amy Gutmann, President, University of Pennsylvania, Re: Illegal Human Experiments Conducted by the EPA, June 8, 2012.

76 Letter from Steve Milloy to Ralph C. Loomis, MD, President, North Carolina Medical Board, June 11, 2012.

77 *See* Letters from Judie B. Clark, Director, Complaint Department, North Carolina Medical Board to Steve Milloy, June 15, 2012.

78 Letter from Steve Milloy to William L. Roper, Dean, School of Medicine, University of North Carolina, June 12, 2012.

79 Letter from William L. Roper to Steve Milloy, June 28, 2012.

80 *See* U.S. Environmental Protection Agency, Letter to Household Member from Martha Sue Carraway and Ana Rappold, Feb 19, 2010.

81 U.S. Environmental Protection Agency, Air quality criteria for particulate matter. Research Triangle Park, NC: National Center for Environmental Assessment-RTP Office; Report Nos. EPA/600/P-95/001aF-cF. 3v, p. 13-92 (1996).

82 At Section 26.111 (a)(1).

83 University of North Carolina-Chapel Hill, Consent to Participate in a Research Study, Adults Subjects, Biomedical Form, September 10, 2009, p. 5.

84 40 *Code of Federal Regulations* 26.116.

85 40 *Code of Federal Regulations* 26.116(a)(2).

86 *See* U.S. Environmental Protection Agency, Final Report: Daily Mortality and Fine and Ultrafine Particles in Erfurt, Germany (EPA Grant Number: R828112C098).

87 University of North Carolina-Chapel Hill, Consent to Participate in a Research Study, Adults Subjects, Biomedical Form, Medical IRB Study #04-1677, August 4, 2010).

88 University of North Carolina-Chapel Hill, Consent to Participate in a Research Study, Adults Subjects, Biomedical Form, Medical IRB Study #07-0190, May 6, 2010.

89 University of North Carolina-Chapel Hill, Consent to Participate in a Research Study, Adults Subjects, Biomedical Form, Medical IRB Study #07-0190, January 5, 2010.

90 40 *Code of Federal Regulations* 26.111(a)(2).

91 40 *Code of Federal Regulations* 26.116.

92 U.S. District Court for the Eastern Division of Virginia (Alexandria Division), Civil Action No. 1:12-cv-1066-AJT-TCB, Statement of Complaint.

93 *Washington Times*, Lawsuit filed against EPA over pollution experiments on humans, September 25, 2012.

94 Milloy S, EPA comments on human testing lawsuit; Claims UNC is 'independent'; Records show otherwise, JunkScience. com, Sep. 26, 2012.

95 Letter from James M. Inhofe to The Honorable Barbara Boxer, September 28, 2012.

96 U.S. House of Representatives, Committee on Government Reform—Minority Staff, Special Investigations Division and U.S. Senate, Office of Sen. Barbara Boxer, Environmental Staff, Human Pesticide Experiments, June 2005.

97 U.S. District Court for the Eastern Division of Virginia (Alexandria Division), Civil Action No. 1:12-cv-1066-AJT-TCB, Memorandum In Opposition To Plaintiff's Motion For Temporary Restraining Order.

98 U.S. District Court for the Eastern Division of Virginia (Alexandria Division), Civil Action No. 1:12-cv-1066-AJT-TCB, Declaration of Martin W. Case.

99 40 *Code of Federal Regulations* 26.117.

100 U.S. District Court for the Eastern Division of Virginia (Alexandria Division), Civil Action No. 1:12-cv-1066-AJT-TCB, Transcript of Emergency Motion for a Temporary Restraining Order, *argued* October 9, 2012.

101 U.S. District Court for the Eastern Division of Virginia (Alexandria Division), Civil Action No. 1:12-cv-1066-AJT-TCB, United States Memorandum in Support of Its Motion to Dismiss, *filed* November 21, 2012.

102 *See* North Carolina Medical Board rife with conflicts of interest in EPA human testing controversy, JunkScience.com, January 29,2013

103 *MIT News*, Student dies at Rochester in MIT-based study, April 10, 1996.

104 *Campus Times* (University of Rochester), UR settles Wan family's lawsuit, October 3, 1996.

105 Zaidi Ali S, Sentimentality and Responsibility in the University, *CovertAction Quarterly*, Spring-Summer 1999.

106 Letter from Rep. Paul Broun, M.D. to Arthur A. Elkins, October 18, 2012.

107 *See* JunkScience.com, EPA Inspector General Announces Investigation of Illegal EPA Human Testing, November 16, 2012.

108 When EPA was sued over its CAPTAIN studies, the agency lowered the maximum age for participants from 75 to 65 years of age.

109 *See* 78 *Federal Register* 3086, January 14, 2013.

110 *See* 78 *Federal Register* 3086, at 3114-3115.

111 40 *Code of Federal Regulations* 26.102(d).

[112] U.S. Environmental Protection Agency, 2008 Progress Report: Human Clinical Studies of Concentrated Ambient Ultrafine and Fine Particles.

[113] JunkScience.com, EPA fails to explain deletion of illegal diesel experiment on children from database, April 25, 2013.

[114] *See* JunkScience.com, EPA Used 10-Year Old Children in Illegal Diesel Exhaust Experiments, January 20, 2015.

[115] California Environmental Protection Agency Air Resources Board, The Report on Diesel Exhaust, as adopted April 22, 1998.

[116] 71 *Federal Register* 36175 (June 23, 2006).

[117] *See* email from Steve Milloy to Sue. S Stewart, Senior Vice President and General Counsel, University of Rochester, Request to suspend illegal human experiments, October 16, 2012.

[118] *See* email from Sue Stewart to Steve Milloy, Re: Request to suspend illegal human experiments, October 19, 2012.

[119] *See* email from Sue Stewart to Steve Milloy, Re: Request to suspend illegal human experiments, November 12, 2012.

[120] *See* email from Christine Burke to Steve Milloy, Re: Request to suspend illegal human experiments, January 23, 2013.

[121] *See* email from Spencer Studwell to Steve Milloy, Re: Request to suspend illegal human experiments, May 15, 2013.

[122] *See* JunkScience.com, New documents show EPA lying to public about air pollution dangers, August 21, 2013.

[123] *See* JunkScience.com, EPA human testing scandal extends to University of Washington; Study subjects not told diesel exhaust can kill, March 12, 2013).

[124] *See* JunkScience.com, University of Washington Letter to Human Guinea Pigs: Oops, we exposed you to **a carcinogen!** March 18, 2013.

[125] Brook RD *et al.*, Particulate Matter Air Pollution and Cardiovascular Disease: An Update to the Scientific Statement from the American Heart Association, *Circulation*, 2010; 121:2331-2378.

[126] American Heart Association, Evidence growing of air pollution's link to heart disease and death, PRNewswire, May 10, 2010.

[127] University of Michigan, Consent to Be Part of a Research Study, Glacier Study #1: Cardiometabolic Effects of Exposure to Differing Mixtures and Concentrations of $PM_{2.5}$ in Obese and Lean Adults.

[128] Payne H, Is the EPA committing deadly human tests? Or just bad policy? *Detroit News*, July 23, 2013.

[129] Letter to the editor, *Detroit News*, July 31, 2013.

[130] JunkScience.com, Michigan medical board refuses to investigate doc who admits to unsafe EPA human experiments, October 14, 2013.

[131] See U.S. Environmental Protection Agency, Office of the Inspector General, Improvements to EPA Policies and Guidance Could Enhance Protection of Human Study Subjects, Report No. 14-P-0154 March 31, 2014.

[132] Associated Press, EPA Fails to Disclose Risks in Human Tests, April 2, 2014.

[133] *New York Times*, E.P.A. Faulted for Failure to Report Risks, April 3, 2014.

134 *Washington* Post, EPA did not disclose cancer risks in tests, April 2, 2014.

135 Milloy S, "The EPA's Secret Whitewash," *Washington Times*, July 24, 2016.

136 U.S. Environmental Protection Agency, Administrator Gina McCarthy, Remarks at the National Academy of Sciences, As Prepared, April 28, 2014.

137 467 *U.S.* 837 (1984).

138 U.S. Government Printing Office, Out Of Thin Air: EPA's Cross-State Air Pollution Rule, Hearing Before The Committee On Science, Space and Technology House Of Representatives, One Hundred Twelfth Congress, First Session, Thursday, September 15, 2011, Serial No. 112-35.

139 Letter from Andy Harris, MD to Gina McCarthy, September 22, 2011.

140 JunkScience.com, Ozone, Asthma Hospitalizations Not Linked in Los Angeles 2009-2011, March 28, 2012.

141 JunkScience.com, Study: Ozone not linked with asthma hospitalizations in major California hospital system, September 3, 2013.

142 See Greven S, Dominici, F, Zeger, S. 2011. An approach to the estimation of chronic air pollution effects using spatio-temporal information. Journal of the American Statistical Association 106:396-406.

143 See JunkScience.com, Airborne Fine Particulate Matter and Short-Term Mortality: Exploring the California Experience, 2007-2010, December 2013.

144 *See* U.S. Environmental Protection Agency, CADDIS, Vol. 4, Exploratory Analysis.

[145] Young SS *et al.*, Air quality and acute deaths in California, 2000-2012, Arxiv.org, revised May 13, 2015 (http://arxiv.org/abs/1502.03062).

[146] *See e.g.,* Lipfert FW *et al.*, The Washington University-EPRI veteran's cohort mortality study: Preliminary results, *Inhalation Toxicology*, 12:41-73, 2000; Lipfert FW *et al.*, Traffic density as a surrogate measure of environmental exposures in studies of air pollution health effects; Long-term mortality in a cohort of U.S. veterans, *Atmospheric Environment*, 40:154-169; Lipfert FW *et al.*, PM constituents and related air quality variable as predictors of survival in a cohort of U.S. military veterans, *Inhalation Toxciology*, 18:645-667; Lipfert FW *et al.*, Air pollution and survival withing the Washington university-EPRI veterans cohort: Risks based on modeled estimates of ambient levels of hazardous and criteria air pollutants, Journal of Air & Waste Management Association, 60:473-489.

[147] Greven S *et al.*, An Approach to the Estimation of Chronic Air Pollution Effects Using Spatio-Temporal Information, *Journal of the American Statistical Association* 106:494:3396-406, June 2011.

[148] *See* Memorandum from Francesca Dominici *et al.* to Bryan Hubbert and Jason Sack, EPA, Reply to: additional information to EPA for these two studies, November 28, 2012.

[149] 78 *Federal Register* 3086, 3115 (January 15, 2013).

[150] *See* Killingsworth CR; Alessandrini F; Krishna Murthy GG; Catalano PJ; Paulauskis JD; Godleski JJ (1997). Inflammation, chemokine expression and death in monocrotaline-treated rats following fuel oil fly ash inhalation. *Inhalation Toxicology* 9: 541-565.

[151] *See* U.S. Environmental Protection Agency, Integrated Science Assessment for Particulate Matter EPA/600/R-081/139F, December 2009.

[152] Ghio AJ *et al.*, Particulate Matter in Cigarette Smoke Alters Iron Homeostasis to Produce a Biological Effect, *American Journal of Respiratory and Critical Care Medicine*, 178:1130-1138, 2008.

[153] See Tzu-Chin W et al., New England Journal of Medicine 318:347-351, February 11, 1988.

[154] U.S. National Institutes of Health, Hookah smoking poses health risks, NIH studies show, *Global Health Matters*, 13:2, March/April 2014.

[155] Gerver Y *et al.*, Smoking Status and Long-Term Survival After First Acute Myocardial Infarction: A Population-Based Cohort Study, *Journal of the American College of Cardiology* 54:25; 2382-7, December 15/22, 2009.

[156] Lindford AJ *et al.*, Home Oxygen Therapy and Cigarette Smoking: a Dangerous Practice, *Annals of Burns and Fires Disasters*, June 30, 2006.

[157] Prabhat J et al., 21st-Century Hazards of Smoking and Benefits of Cessation in the United States, New England Journal of Medicine 2013; 368:341-350, January 24, 2013.

[158] This calculation was made as follows: 40,000 millionths-of-a-gram of $PM_{2.5}$ per cigarette x 20 cigarettes per day (about the average level of smoking by study subjects) x 365 days x 15 years (assume smoking between ages 20-35) = 4.38 billion millionths-of-a-gram of $PM_{2.5}$.

[159] Kleipes NE *et al.*, Real-Time Measurement of Outdoor Tobacco Smoke Particles, *Journal of the Air & Waste Management Association*, 57:5, 522-534, 2007.

160 California Environmental Protection Agency Air Resources Board, Secondhand Smoke in Cars Fact Sheet.

161 Zhou S, Air Quality in New York City Hookah Bars, *Tobacco Control,* September 16 2014.

162 Repace JL *et al.,* Air pollution in Boston bars before and after a smoking ban, *BMC Public Health.* 2006 Oct 27; 6:266.

163 *See* U.S. Environmental Protection Agency, Respiratory Health Effects of Passive Smoking: Lung Cancer and Other Disorders, EPA/600/6-90/006F, December 1992.

164 Pope III, CA *et al.*, Cardiovascular Mortality and Exposure to Airborne Fine Particulate Matter and Cigarette Smoke. *Circulation* 120:941-948 (2009).

165 *See e.g.,* Landen DD, Coal Dust Exposure and Mortality From Ischemic Heart Disease Among a Cohort of U.S. Coal Miners, *American Journal of Industrial Medicine* 54(10):727-33.

166 *See* 79 *Federal Register* 24813 (May 1, 2014).

167 Attfield MD and Kuemple ED, Mortality Among U.S. Underground Coal Miners: A 23-Year Follow-Up, *American Journal of Industrial Medicine* 51:231-245 (2008).

168 Attfield MD *et al.*, The Diesel Exhaust in Miners Study: A Cohort Mortality Study With Emphasis on Lung Cancer, *Journal of the National Cancer Institute* 2012 June 6; 104(11): 869–883.

169 Garshick E *et al.*, Lung Cancer in Railroad Workers Exposed to Diesel Exhaust, *Environmental Health Perspectives* 112(15): 1539–1543.

170 Laden F, Cause-specific mortality in the unionized U.S. trucking industry, *Environmental Health Perspectives* 115(8):1192-6.

[171] Nemery B *et al.*, The Meuse Valley Fog of 1930; An Air Pollution Disaster, *Lancet* 357: 704-708, March 3, 2001.

[172] U.S. Environmental Protection Agency Office of Air Quality Planning and Standards, Review of the National Ambient Air Quality Standards for Particulate Matter: Policy Assessment of Scientific and Technical Information, External Review Draft, November 1995.

[173] U.S. Public Health Service, Air Pollution in Donora, PA: Epidemiology of the Unusual Smog Episode of October 1948, Preliminary Report, Public Health Bulletin No. 306, 1949.

[174] *See* 36 *Federal Register* 8186 (April 30, 1971).

[175] Air Pollution in Donora, Pa.: Epidemiology of the Unusual Smog Episode of October 1948. Preliminary Report, *Journal of the American Medical Association* 143(3):323.

[176] See Bell M et al., A Retrospective Assessment of Mortality from the London Smog Episode of 1952: The Role of Influenza and Pollution, *Environmental Health Perspectives*, 112:1.

[177] Smog Masks, *British Medical Journal* 2:1145-46, November 21, 1953.

[178] *See e.g.,* Blanket of smog in Beijing hits start of Lunar New Year getaway, *South China Post*, January 16, 2014.

[179] Milloy S, China's Bad Air Pits the Lie to EPA Scare Tactics, *Washington Times*, January 22, 2013.

[180] *China Daily*, Life expectancy for Beijing residents increases, July 12, 2013.

[181] Rohde R and Muller R, Air Pollution in China: Mapping of Concentrations and Sources, PLoS One, August 20, 2015.

[182] Based on personal calculations from documents contained in the EPA's research grants database.

[183] Milloy S, Clearing the Air on EPA, *Washington Times*, March 8, 2012.

[184] *See* Letter from George T. Wolff, Chair, CASAC, to Carol M. Browner, Administrator, EPA, March 15, 1996.

[185] *See* Sutter JD, EPA Boss: Climate Change Could Kill Thousands, CNN.com, June 22, 2015.

[186] *See* Milloy S, Media beats up Willie Soon, but turns a blind eye to EPA-funded researchers shilling for EPA's biggest rule, JunkScience.com, May 5, 2015.

[187] *See* Milloy S, E-mails show Harvard, Syracuse universities, researchers falsely claimed no EPA involvement in Clean Power Plan study, JunkScience.com, June 3, 2015.

[188] *See e.g.,* Lipton E and Davenport C, Critics Hear E.P.A.'s Voice in 'Public Comments,' *New York Times*, May 18, 2015; Davenport C, Taking Oil Industry Cue, Environmentalists Drew Emissions Blueprint, *New York Times*, July 6, 2014; and Bradley R, Sue and Settle Shenanigans, *The Hill*, September 2, 2015.

[189] *See American Lung Association v. Browner*, 884 *F. Supp* 345 (D. Ariz. 1994).

[190] Milloy S, EPA owns the American Lung Association, JunkScience.com, March 15, 2011.

[191] *See* Milloy S, EPA-American Lung Association: Axis of Junk Science, JunkScience.com, September 8, 2011.

[192] *See* U.S. Environmental Protection Agency, TODAY: EPA, American Lung Association to Hold Press Conference to Discuss Mercury and Air Toxics Standards (Media Release), March 16, 2011.

[193] *See* Milloy S, American Lung Association runs another fake air pollution ad, JunkScience.com, July 16, 2011.

[194] See American Lung Association, American Lung Association Releases New Television Ad to Thwart Congressional Attacks on the Clean Air Act (Media Release), July 18, 2011.

[195] *See* Milloy S, JunkScience.com torpedoes American Lung Association at Senate hearing, JunkScience.com, June 8, 2011.

[196] *See* Milloy S, House: EPA in default of 'secret science' subpoena, JunkScience.com, September 3, 2013.

[197] Cama T, Supreme Court defeat won't hinder climate push, says EPA chief, *The Hill*, July 7, 2015.

[198] *See* White House, A Blueprint for New Beginnings: A Responsible Budget for Americas Priorities, U.S. Government Printing Office, Washington, D.C. 2001.

[199] U.S. Senate Committee on Environment and Public Works (Minority Report), EPA's Playbook Revealed: A Story of Fraud, Deceit and Secret Science, March 19, 2014.

ABOUT THE AUTHOR

Steve Milloy is a recognized leader in the fight against junk science with more than 25 years of experience and accomplishment. Credited with popularizing the term "junk science," Mr. Milloy is the founder and publisher of the award-winning web site JunkScience.com and wrote the popular "Junk Science" column for FOXNews.com during 2000-2009. He is an expert on energy, environmental and public health issues, a public affairs consultant, author, TV/radio commentator and public speaker. Milloy was trained in natural sciences, biostatistics, law and securities regulation. He has also been an attorney for the U.S. Securities and Exchange Commission, a registered securities principal, investment fund manager, non-profit executive, print/web columnist on science and business issues, and coal company executive. Mr. Milloy's work has been endorsed by some of America's most elite scientists including Philip Abelson, Phd (Editor, Science, 1962-1984, winner of the National Medal of Science, Co-discoverer of Neptunium), Donald H. Henderson, MD (Dean, Johns Hopkins School of Public Health, 1977-1990, Director, UN Global Smallpox Eradication Program, National Medal of Science) and Frederick Seitz, PhD (First President, National Academy of Sciences).

Made in the USA
Middletown, DE
26 April 2017